Change Over Time

How Populations and Species Change

SCHOLASTIC SCIENCE PLACE

DEVELOPED IN COOPERATION

WITH

DENVER MUSEUM OF NATURAL HISTORY

DENVER, COLORADO

Founded in 1900, the Denver Museum of Natural History is a recognized leader in applying educational research, creating innovative programs, exhibits, and publications, and encouraging lifelong learning in the cultural, natural, and health sciences. The museum also offers animal habitat dioramas, the interactive Hall of Life, the Planetarium and IMAX theater, and the Prehistoric Journey which covers the three and a half billion year history of life on Earth.

Copyright © 1995 by Scholastic Inc.   All rights reserved. Published by Scholastic Inc.   Printed in the U.S.A.
ISBN 0-590-27707-3
1 2 3 4 5 6 7 8 9 10   09   01 00 99 98 97 96 95

CONTENTS

Change Over Time

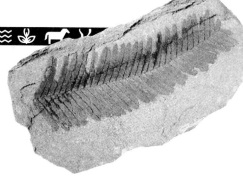

► SUBCONCEPT: Changes in the environment or human intervention can result in changes in the characteristics of a population, which are passed on to succeeding generations.

(continued on next page)

CONTENTS

Hands-On and Media Resources

Students can use the following tools as they explore evolution.

EQUIPMENT KITS

Inside the bag you'll find the Nonconsumable Equipment Kit, which includes all the nonconsumable equipment you'll need to do the Explorations. Also available is an optional Consumable Equipment Kit, which includes all the materials you're not likely to have on hand.

VIDEO: A PROBLEM-SOLVING MYSTERY

Challenge students to work alongside the famous Science Sleuths as they use their science expertise to solve some puzzling problems.

REFERENCE LITERATURE

Students use these additional resources to extend their understanding of the concepts developed in particular lessons: *Dinosaurs Walked Here,* by Patricia Lauber; *Charles Darwin and Evolution,* by Steve Parker.

INSTRUCTIONAL SUPPORT

These include Home Connection Collection™, ScienceMats, and Recording Board.

OPTIONAL
SCHOLASTIC NETWORK

Throughout this Teacher's Map you'll see places where you and your students can connect with schools across the country. These are opportunities for your students to share data and ideas and to connect to a world of information.

UNIT PLANNING GUIDE ....

LESSON	TIME	EXPLORATION / MATERIALS	COMPONENTS	PROCESS SKILLS
1 That's Life! (pp. 8–11)	One 40-minute session		Student's Map pages 4–5, ThinkMat 1, *For Science Browsers*, The Video *Change Over Time*	
2 What Are Fossils? (pp. 12–19)	Two 40-minute sessions	**Examine a genuine fossil.** fossil kit, hand lens, ruler **Solve a fossil puzzle.** punch-out fossil kit	Student's Map pages 6–9, LabMats 2A and 2B, ThinkMat 2, *Dinosaurs Walked Here*	observing, measuring, comparing, communicating, making models, ordering, hypothesizing
3 How Do Fossils Form? (pp. 20–27)	One 50-minute session and one 45-minute session; both Explorations require waiting time	**Make a fossil with clay and sand.** margarine tub, petroleum jelly, water, cups, tablespoon, plaster, powdered clay, sand, leaves, feathers, thin objects **Make a see-through fossil.** petroleum jelly, mucilage, small paper cup, dried bee	Student's Map pages 10–13, LabMats 3A and 3B, ThinkMat 3, *Dinosaurs Walked Here*	making models, observing, comparing, communicating, predicting
4 How Can You Decide Which Fossils Are Older? (pp. 28–35)	One 50-minute session	**Watch time fly in the Grand Canyon.** ThinkMat 4, scissors	Student's Map pages 14–17, LabMat 4, ThinkMat 4, *Dinosaurs Walked Here*	observing, comparing, predicting
5 How Do Fossils Show the History of Earth's Species? (pp. 36–43)	One 50-minute session and one 45-minute session	**Make a time line.** 15-m (50-ft) roll of adding machine paper or newsprint, ruler, tape, markers or crayons **Find your fossil in time.** fossils from Lesson 2, classroom time line	Student's Map pages 18–21, LabMats 5A and 5B, ThinkMat 5	ordering, measuring, comparing, communicating, interpreting data
6 What Happened to the Dinosaurs? (pp. 44–51)	One 40–minute session		Student's Map pages 22–25, ThinkMat 6	
7 What Affects the Size of a Population? (pp. 52–59)	One 40-minute session and one 45-minute session	**Make a population model.** 3 sheets of paper, coins, scissors **Play Rabbit and Fox.** scissors, ThinkMat 7, number cube	Student's Map Pages 26–29, LabMats 7A and 7B, ThinkMat 7	predicting, comparing, communicating
8 How Do Members of a Population Differ and Compete? (pp. 60–67)	One 50-minute session	**Sort and measure peanuts.** 40 unshelled peanuts, ruler, ThinkMat 8	Student's Map pages 30–33, LabMat 8, ThinkMat 8	observing, communicating, measuring
9 How Are Traits Passed From Parents to Offspring? (pp. 68–75)	One 50-minute session	**Make a model of a cat family.** 2 coins, paper, scissors, marker, tape, LabMat 9	Student's Map pages 34–37, LabMat 9, ThinkMat 9	communicating, comparing, predicting, categorizing

LESSON	TIME	EXPLORATION / MATERIALS	COMPONENTS	PROCESS SKILLS
❿ What Is Artificial Selection? (pp. 76–83)	One 50-minute session	**Make a faster rabbit.** number cube, paper, pencil	Student's Map pages 38–41, LabMat 10, ThinkMat 10	communicating, comparing
⓫ How Are Species Selected Naturally? (pp. 84–91)	Two 45-minute sessions	**May the best eater win.** black paper; white, red, spotted, and black beans; plastic cups; spoon; fork; clothespin; watch with second hand **Return to Rabbit Island.** ThinkMat 11, scissors, pencil or pen	Student's Map pages 42–45, LabMats 11A and 11B, ThinkMat 11, *Charles Darwin and Evolution*	observing, communicating, comparing, predicting
⓬ How Could New Species Develop? (pp. 92–99)	One 45-minute session		Student's Map pages 46–49, ThinkMat 12, *Charles Darwin and Evolution*	
⓭ How Are Species Related to Each Other? (pp. 100–107)	Two 50-minute sessions	**Make models of forelimbs.** modeling clay **Compare old and new skeletons.** ThinkMat 13, modeling clay, tape, toothpicks	Student's Map pages 50–53, LabMats 13A and 13B, ThinkMat 13	observing, comparing, communicating
⓮ Are Species Changing Today? (pp. 108–115)	One 40-minute session	**Design the animals of the future.** ThinkMat 14	Student's Map pages 54–57, LabMat 14, ThinkMat 14, *Charles Darwin and Evolution*	predicting, comparing

Think Tank: Designing Future Organisms
TIME: At least three 45-minute sessions. Can be expanded.

LESSON	SUMMARY
⓯ Identify Problems	Teams identify the problems they'd face as scientists trying to design organisms of the future.
⓰ Find Solutions	Teams study the evolution of the horse to help them design future organisms. They'll also use tables to organize information.
⓱ Make Models	Teams brainstorm a list of features for designing a community of organisms of the future. Their models reflect what they've learned about inherited traits and natural selection.

⓲ Unit Assessment Options

Baseline Assessment:	In Lesson 1 students write three journal entries, imagining they have traveled back in time. By repeating the same assignment in Lesson 18, they can see what they've learned.
Performance Assessment:	Students demonstrate process skills and their grasp of the unit concepts by making models of bones of an animal that might have lived on Earth.
Connected Thinking Assessment:	Students demonstrate thinking skills and their grasp of the unit concepts by writing an essay about two possible fates of their future organisms.
Portfolio Assessment:	Students put together their best work at the end of the unit. Ideas for what to include in Portfolios appear throughout the unit.
Written Tests:	ThinkMats 5, 10, 14, and 18 provide a way to assess students' understanding of each subconcept and the unit as a whole.

That's Life!

Lesson Road Map

In this lesson: Students begin their exploration of evolution by reading and discussing an article about dinosaurs and watching a video.

In the next lesson: Students will explore how fossils tell us about the past.

Getting Organized

This lesson requires about 40 minutes, including 15 minutes for watching the video.

Materials per Group:
Paper
Pencils

Advance Preparation:
Read Lesson 18, Unit Assessment.

The Story Line

Grade Level Concept
Different species have inhabited the earth at different times.

Subconcepts
Fossils provide evidence that many species that once inhabited the earth have become extinct.

Changes in the environment or human intervention can result in changes in the characteristics of a population, which are passed on to succeeding generations.

Variation and natural selection have resulted in the evolution of new species.

Lesson Concept
Every living thing on the earth undergoes changes, some rapid and some much more gradual.

ALSO FOR THIS LESSON

ThinkMat 1

Introduces the unit

For Science Browsers

"Scientists Dig Up New Dinosaurs" Student page 65

Reference Literature Synopses

As students work through this unit, they will be acquiring information about how living organisms on the earth have evolved and how evolution is studied. For example, by referring to the reference literature, such as *Dinosaurs Walked Here,* students will find out how fossils are formed and how they can tell us about the past. The photographs and illustrations in *Charles Darwin and Evolution* give students a vivid picture of Darwin's research on the origin of species.

Dinosaurs Walked Here by Patricia Lauber

Charles Darwin and Evolution by Steve Parker

Video Synopsis

There's a problem to be solved and the Science Sleuths are on the case. The population of a Fast Fish breeder's tank is changing over time. And it's not growing. The spotted fish are vanishing. As the Sleuths investigate, students are introduced to the problems of disease on small populations, genetics, and possible predators. Who can explain the strange case of the Fast Fish Frenzy? (It turns out that a predator cat is making off with the easy-to-spot-and-catch spotted fish. The gold-colored fish blend in with the tank.)

Unit Vocabulary

adaptation, artificial selection, evolution, extinction, fossil record, fossil, genes, geological period, mutation, natural selection, paleontologist, population, radioactive dating, sedimentation, species, trait, variations

Theme Connection: Patterns of Change

As long as living things have existed on the earth, they have undergone changes in which new species have developed from already existing ones. Similarly, the structures of the earth's crust are constantly changing, shaping into new landforms.

Baseline Assessment

The Baseline Assessment helps you evaluate where students are conceptually as you begin the unit. By repeating the same assessment task at the end of the unit, you'll be able to see the growth in each student's understanding. Students, too, will be able to evaluate their own progress.

Invite students to pretend they are taking a ride in a machine that will carry them back through time. Have them write three journal entries describing the kinds of living things they see. One entry should be for 10,000 years ago, one for 140 million years ago, and one for a time just after the earth came into existence. Save these journal entries to use in Lesson 18, Unit Assessment.

ACTIVATE:
Change Over Time

Opening the Discussion

After you've finished the Baseline Assessment and collected students' journals, encourage students to talk about changes they have seen in themselves, their parents and grandparents, and in their pets.

Ask: **What are some of the ways you and the people and animals around you are changing?** *(Students will probably mention physical changes and the development of both mental and physical skills. They may say something about aging in their family members.)*

Explain that living things change throughout their lives. **Do you think the living things on Earth have always been the same? Why or why not?** *(Students will probably know that some animals such as dinosaurs have disappeared.)*

Have students read the introductory paragraphs on page 4. **What have you learned from books, television, and movies about how living things on the earth have changed over time?** *(Invite students to say what they've learned.)*

Discuss the boxed questions with students. Encourage each student to contribute to the list of things they already know about the ways living things change over time. Write their responses on the Recording Board.

Student Pages 4–5

Using Scientific Methods

Ask students if any of their questions about changes of living things on the earth appear in the table of contents. Explain that as they explore the answers to these questions, they'll use the scientific methods described on page 5. If necessary, define the terms *hypothesis, hands-on exploration, data,* and *apply.* Emphasize that even though science is fun, students will need to record data precisely.

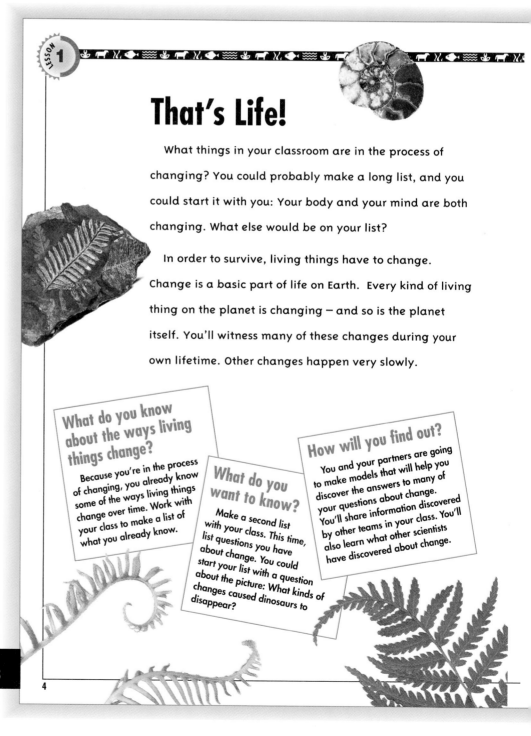

That's Life!

What things in your classroom are in the process of changing? You could probably make a long list, and you could start it with you: Your body and your mind are both changing. What else would be on your list?

In order to survive, living things have to change. Change is a basic part of life on Earth. Every kind of living thing on the planet is changing — and so is the planet itself. You'll witness many of these changes during your own lifetime. Other changes happen very slowly.

What do you know about the ways living things change?

Because you're in the process of changing, you already know some of the ways living things change over time. Work with your class to make a list of what you already know.

What do you want to know?

Make a second list with your class. This time, list questions you have about change. You could start your list with a question about the picture: What kinds of changes caused dinosaurs to disappear?

How will you find out?

You and your partners are going to make models that will help you discover the answers to many of your questions about change. You'll share information discovered by other teams in your class. You'll also learn what other scientists have discovered about change.

4

Introducing *For Science Browsers*

Ask students to turn to the article "Scientists Dig Up New Dinosaurs" on page 65 in the *For Science Browsers* section of their books. (This section begins on page 130 of the Teacher's Map.) Ask: **Why are dinosaurs making news now?** *(Different kinds of dinosaur skeletons and fossils have been discovered and research is now taking place in more countries.)* When you finish reading the article, ask: **Why is the discovery of Eoraptor important?** *(It tells us what the earliest dinosaurs were like.)*

Using the Video

1. The video is one option for Baseline Assessment. As the Sleuths present the mystery and do their detective work, students will think of possible solutions. Tell students to write down their predictions and store them in their Portfolio. Later in the unit—before your class goes to work on the Think Tank—show the video again. After doing the Explorations in Lessons 2–14, your students will have a much different reaction to the video content. Have them record their new solutions and compare them with their solutions from the first viewing.

2. If you want to use the Baseline Assessment suggested on page 9, remember that the video is also a great way to introduce the unit topic. Let it roll after you've introduced *For Science Browsers*.

This is a good opportunity to have students share ideas about how living things evolve.

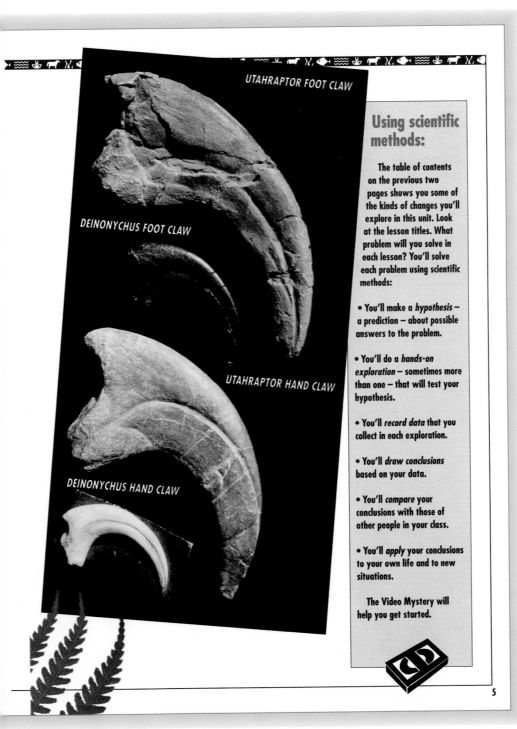

UTAHRAPTOR FOOT CLAW

DEINONYCHUS FOOT CLAW

UTAHRAPTOR HAND CLAW

DEINONYCHUS HAND CLAW

Using scientific methods:

The table of contents on the previous two pages shows you some of the kinds of changes you'll explore in this unit. Look at the lesson titles. What problem will you solve in each lesson? You'll solve each problem using scientific methods:

• You'll make a *hypothesis* – a prediction – about possible answers to the problem.

• You'll do a *hands-on exploration* – sometimes more than one – that will test your hypothesis.

• You'll *record data* that you collect in each exploration.

• You'll draw *conclusions* based on your data.

• You'll *compare* your conclusions with those of other people in your class.

• You'll *apply* your conclusions to your own life and to new situations.

The Video Mystery will help you get started.

5

What Are Fossils?

Student Pages 6-9

Lesson Road Map

In the last lesson: Students began their exploration of evolution by reading and discussing an article about dinosaurs and watching a video.

In this lesson: Students explore how fossils tell us about the past. In Part One they observe fossils and draw conclusions about them. In Part Two they use a puzzle to reconstruct an extinct animal.

In the next lesson: Students will observe how fossils form.

The Story Line

▽ Grade Level Concept
Different species have inhabited the earth at different times.

▽ Subconcepts
Fossils provide evidence that many species that once inhabited the earth have become extinct.

Changes in the environment or human intervention can result in changes in the characteristics of a population, which are passed on to succeeding generations.

Variation and natural selection have resulted in the evolution of new species.

▽ Lesson Concept
Fossils are traces or remains of organisms that lived long ago, which tell us about the earth's past.

Getting Organized

This lesson requires two 40-minute sessions.

Materials per Group:
Fossil kit
Hand lens
Ruler

PART ONE

Advance Preparation: Gather materials.

Materials per Group:
Punch-out fossil kit

PART TWO

Advance Preparation: Gather materials.

ALSO FOR THIS LESSON:

ThinkMat 2

Thinking activity about the lesson

Pages 2–6

LabMats 2A and 2B

Recording sheets for the Explorations

For Science Browsers

"Dinosaurs—My Life's Work" Student page 66

Content Background

Fossils are the remains or traces of organisms that lived long ago, from which scientists piece together information about the past. How have species changed over time? Paleontologists have found the answers to such a question through fossils. The word *fossil* comes from the Latin *fossilis*, meaning "dug up." Most fossils are found in sedimentary rock, but fossils can also be found preserved in tar, amber (hardened tree sap), and ice.

By comparing fossils and living species, paleontologists can make guesses about extinct species. Some paleontologists believe that dinosaurs raised their young the same way birds do because fossils of dinosaur eggs and young dinosaurs have been found in nests. Climatic and geological changes can also show up in the fossil record. Fossils of tropical forests have been found in Antarctica, which means that its climate has changed tremendously.

For fossilization to take place, an organism's remains must be buried beneath soil or other natural substances and then left undisturbed. Since these conditions occur infrequently, most living things leave no fossil record of their existence. Whole organisms are rarely preserved by fossilization. Usually fossils are formed from just the hard parts of organisms, such as bones, shells, teeth, or stems, which take longer to decay than the soft parts. In some cases all you'll see is a fossilized imprint of the organism, rather than a fossil of the organism itself.

Vocabulary

fossil: The remains or traces of plants and animals from the earth's past.

traits: Characteristics of an individual organism, such as eye color.

species: A group of organisms that share characteristics and can breed together naturally.

fossil record: All known fossils, taken together.

paleontologist: A scientist who studies fossils.

Theme Connection: Patterns of Change

Fossils provide clues about the kinds of organisms that inhabited Earth in the past and about the changes in species that have occurred since life on Earth began. Landforms also provide clues to some of the changes that have occurred to the earth's surface such as weathering, erosion, and deposition.

Considering Second-Language Learners

Help develop students' command of simple past tenses in English by guiding them through a reading of the lesson, pausing when a verb in the past tense appears, such as *lived, existed, looked, was, discover.* Ask students to write questions for past tense sentences in the lesson. For example: "Because of fossils like the ones in the photos, we know dinosaurs once roamed a plant-covered Earth." A question that could be answered with such a statement would be: "How do we know dinosaurs once existed on Earth?" Ask students to write their questions on cards or pieces of paper and trade them. They'll then take turns reading and answering questions.

Naive Conceptions

Students may think that all fossils are complete organisms preserved in one piece. This lesson shows that most fossils are parts of organisms.

LESSON 2 **Part One**

What do we know?
What do we want to know?

1

ACTIVATE

EXPLORATION:
Examine a genuine fossil.

Process Skills and Objectives

Students will:

- **observe** that their fossils resemble living organisms

- **measure** their fossils to try to find out what type of organism it is

- **compare** how their fossils look to what the organism looked like

- **communicate** their ideas and interpretations about the appearance of their fossils and the environment where the organisms lived

Opening the Discussion

Have students read the introductory paragraph on page 6. Ask: **Where have you seen life-size replicas or very lifelike depictions of prehistoric animals and plants?** *(Possible answers include: natural history museums, films, magazines, theme parks.)*

Where do you think natural history museums get the information to re-create prehistoric animals? *(They get their information by examining actual bones and fossils.)*

How much is fact and how much is imagination? *(Since museum models are based on scientific evidence, they're fairly accurate, but there are a lot of missing pieces that scientists must guess.)* Write students' ideas on the Recording Board.

PREPARING FOR THE EXPLORATION

Materials per Group: fossil kit, hand lens, ruler

Suggested Grouping: eight

Approximate Time: 20 minutes

Classroom Management: Copy LabMat 2A. Since the first Exploration leads into the second, you shouldn't jigsaw the two. Allow groups to trade fossils.

LESSON 2

What Are Fossils?

How would you like to find yourself face to face in the hall with a birdlike creature the size of a minivan that eats raw red meat for breakfast? You've seen pictures of dinosaurs, prehistoric birds, and strange-looking plants that lived on Earth millions of years ago. But where's the evidence that these things really existed?

Exploration:
Examine a genuine <u>fossil</u>.

You need:
Fossil kit
Hand lens
Ruler

❶ What does your fossil look like? Describe its shape and color. Touch your fossil. Does it feel rough or smooth? Record your observations on your Labmat.

❷ Measure the length, width, and height of your fossil. Record your data.

❸ Use the hand lens to make closer observations of your fossil. Look at it from all sides. Draw a detailed sketch of what you see.

Interpret your results.

- Fossils are remains or traces of plants and animals from the earth's past. How do your observations support this statement? What were some of the clues that indicated you were observing a fossil?

- Do you think your fossil was a plant or an animal? Is it the remains of an entire living thing or part of a living thing? Give reasons for your choices.

- Draw a picture of what you think your fossil organism looked like when it was alive. What are its physical <u>traits</u>, or characteristics? Why do you think so?

- Fossils form in different ways. What does your fossil appear to be made of?

6 SUBCONCEPT ONE: FOSSILS AND EXTINCT SPECIES

Student Pages 6–7

EXPLORATION:
Examine a genuine fossil.

❶ Have students compare the fossils to familiar living plants or animals. Distribute LabMat 2A.

❷ Students will probably decide which measure is length and which is height based on what they think their fossil organism is.

❸ Ask: **Why would accurate drawings and measurements be useful to scientists learning about ancient organisms?** *(They*

would help scientists re-create and find out more about the organisms.)

Interpret Your Results

- Depends on the fossil, but students will probably recognize plant or animal parts, such as a piece of shell, wood, grain, and so on.
- Students may say they don't know what the fossil was. Encourage them to speculate and make reasonable guesses.
- Drawings will vary, but have students explain what clues from the fossils helped them envision what the organism once looked like.
- Most of the fossils will appear to be made of rock.

Exploration Connection:
Using reference books

From the map, students will see that Nebraska was once covered by the Western

Interior Seaway. Students will probably also realize that the discovery of fossils of sea plants and animals helped scientists to conclude how much of North America was covered by water. Ask: **How has the land in our state changed? Did it once have a coastline?** *(From the map students will be able to note any differences.)*

In *Dinosaurs Walked Here* students will discover that some things haven't changed—large prehistoric fish ate smaller fish. The horseshoe crab fossil shows that some species haven't changed much over millions of years.

**LAND AND WATER OF NORTH AMERICA
74 MILLION YEARS AGO**

◀ Seventy-four million years ago, water covered a large part of North America. How could fossils have helped scientists discover this? What do you think it looked like where you live?

◀ Remains of leaves *(left)* and dinosaur eggs *(below)* are two pieces of the <u>fossil record</u>, a time line of living things based on fossil evidence.

Exploration Connection:
Using reference books

Most animals and plants die without leaving a trace.

Luckily for us, though, some organisms leave a record of their existence. Because of fossils like the ones in the photos, we know dinosaurs once roamed a plant-covered earth. We also know the earth has changed a lot over time.

Look at the map. How can it help explain a fossil seashell found in Nebraska?

Together, all the fossils that have ever been found make up the fossil record—the longest and best history of the earth's past <u>species</u>. A species is a group of organisms that share many traits and can breed together naturally.

Look at the fossils pictured on pages 2–6 of *Dinosaurs Walked Here*. What does the fossil on page 6 tell you about prehistoric fish? Which fossil do you think looks the most like a species that is alive today?

7

EXPLORATION:
Solve a fossil puzzle.

Process Skills and Objectives

Students will:

• **make models** of the skeletal structure of a dinosaur

• **order** the bones into groups of specific body parts

• **compare** the forms of the dinosaur bones with the parts of the dinosaur in the illustration

• **hypothesize** about the features and color of the dinosaur

PREPARING FOR THE EXPLORATION

Materials per Group: punch-out fossil kit

Suggested Grouping: four

Approximate Time: 20 minutes

Classroom Management: Copy LabMat 2B. Allow enough space for each group to spread out.

EXPLORATION:
Solve a fossil puzzle.

❶ Make sure students don't mix their puzzle pieces with those of other students. Distribute LabMat 2B.

❷ ❸ Encourage students to sort the bones into groups. Have them sort the leg bones into one group and the tailbones into another.

❹ Encourage students to consider where the dinosaur may have lived, what kind of food it ate,

and how it moved around. Have students use what they know about other animals to imagine what the dinosaur may have looked like. Tell them to consider the adaptations of other animals. Ask: **Was the dinosaur's skin the color of its surroundings to help camouflage it? Or was its skin brightly colored to help it attract a mate?**

🌀 **Troubleshooting:** You may want to pair students who have difficulty with mechanics or thinking visually with students who don't so that they can help one another.

---

2 What Are Fossils?

Small fossils are often found in one piece. But scientists have rebuilt some of the largest fossils from scattered clues and broken pieces. You're going to rebuild an entire animal from fossil clues yourself. Imagine how much harder the job would be if you had to find the pieces in a baking-hot desert or a windy canyon—when you don't even know what kind of creature the pieces belong to. Which piece goes where?

► A paleontologist carefully separates fossilized dinosaur bones from the surrounding rock.

Exploration:
Solve a fossil puzzle.

You need:
Punch-out fossil kit

❶ Punch out the dinosaur bones along their perforated edges.

❷ Look at the picture of the dinosaur and decide how its bones might fit together.

❸ Build your dinosaur skeleton bone by bone.

❹ No one really knows exactly what any of the dinosaurs looked like with skin on the bones, so your idea of what your dinosaur looked like alive doesn't have to agree with the illustrator's idea. Draw a picture of your dinosaur and write down why you chose its colors and other traits. ✏️

Interpret your results.

• How did you figure out how to put the bones together? What clues helped you? Did you think about the bones of other animals you know?

• How do you think your dinosaur moved about? What clues led you to conclude this?

• Do you think your dinosaur was able to fly? How can you tell?

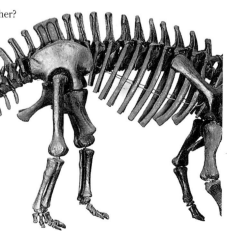

Student Pages 8–9

8 SUBCONCEPT ONE: FOSSILS AND EXTINCT SPECIES

Interpret Your Results

- The dinosaur picture and the shapes of the bones will help students determine how to connect the bones.
- By examining the positions and sizes of the fossil bones and comparing those bones with the skeletons of animals they already know about, students will be able to make predictions about how the animal could have moved.
- No, they don't seem to have wing bones.

Closer to Home: The big dinosaur mix-up

Explain to students that fossils are only clues to past life. No one knows exactly what dinosaurs looked like or how they lived. Since these animals are extinct, even scientists who examine the same fossils come up with different ideas about dinosaurs.

After students have read the text, ask : **What do you think other scientists learned from this incident?** *(They probably won't jump to the same conclusion so quickly.)*

- He wasn't able to make many comparisons.

- Accept any reasonable answer. Explain that dinosaur bones are often found jumbled at a site, but this one was complete except for the head.

- There were no fossils of sea animals or plants found near the fossils of the Apatosauros.

- The answers to this question may yield some insight into the child's ability to deal with making a mistake.

This is a good time to distribute ThinkMat 2.

Think!

Both paleontologists and detectives search for clues. They examine the scene, using scientific tools and techniques.

▲ *Apatosaurus* as it might have looked alive

▼ *Apatosaurus* skeleton

Think!

How is a paleontologist's job like detective work?

Closer to Home:
The big dinosaur mix-up

Everyone makes mistakes—even scientists. One well-known scientific mistake involved a team of <u>paleontologists</u>—scientists who study fossils—and a dinosaur they called *Brontosaurus*.

For many years, *Brontosaurus* was thought to be a plant-eater with a small head and an enormous body—a body so large that it had to stay in the water to hold itself up. *Brontosaurus* had the bone structure of *Apatosaurus*, a dinosaur discovered two years earlier. But *Brontosaurus* had a different head, and its body was much larger than *Apatosaurus*'s body. The same team of paleontologists, led by Othniel Charles Marsh, had discovered both dinosaurs.

Most dinosaur fossils are not found complete, and *Brontosaurus* was missing its head. But a few kilometers away, Marsh and his team found some likely jawbones. With the head in place, the team had a dinosaur different from *Apatosaurus*. Thinking they had discovered a new species, they gave it a new name—*Brontosaurus*.

Years later, with the discovery of more *Apatosaurus* fossils, the mix-up became clear. *Brontosaurus* was simply a full-grown, adult *Apatosaurus* — with a head borrowed from an entirely different dinosaur.

- How would the fact that so few *Apatosaurus* fossils had been discovered help explain Marsh's confusion?

- Do you think that creating a head based on jawbones found so far away was a good idea? Why or why not?

- After Marsh's discoveries, new fossil evidence suggested that *Apatosaurus* lived on the land. What might this evidence have been?

- If you believed something very strongly and new evidence appeared that showed you might be mistaken, how would you respond?

9

LESSON THINKING SKILLS:
Recognizing Patterns and Relationships;
Drawing Conclusions

Assessment Options

Using Students' Process Performance and Recorded Observations

Written Options

1. Students' responses on their LabMats and ThinkMat should give you a clear idea of their understanding of the lesson concept. Use Student Benchmarks to analyze their answers.

2. Have students use their recorded observations from Exploration 1 to write a journal entry. Tell them to imagine that they are scientists who have just found the fossil. Where, when, what, why, and how did they find the fossil?

Student Benchmarks

Proficient: Students explain that fossils are traces or remains of once-living organisms. By examining fossils, they'll be able to discuss how the organism looked and the type of environment in which it lived.

Apprentice: Students relate their fossils to living organisms that they are familiar with.

Novice: Students discuss how fossils can tell us about the past but may not be able to identify their fossils.

Portfolio

Students may want to include the LabMats and the journal entries from the Written Options from this lesson in their Portfolio.

Oral Options

Listen to students as they do the Explorations. Student Benchmarks will give you an idea of how well they understand the lesson concept.

1. In Part One, ask students how they determined whether their fossils were animals or plants. From their observations, did the fossils resemble any plants or animals they're familiar with?

2. In Part Two, ask students how the fossil puzzle is different from the fossil they examined in Part One. Discuss how the puzzle is a model while the fossil is a real sample of a once-living organism.

3. How students answer the Closer to Home questions will also give you a good idea of their understanding of the lesson concept.

The following questions can also be used to assess understanding of the lesson concept:

4. Why is it important for paleontologists to share their theories and discoveries? *(More accurate conclusions can be drawn with more information and more minds working together.)*

5. Why do paleontologists also need to understand zoology, botany, and geology? *(They have to know about the animals, plants, and the earth of the present to make connections to those of the past.)*

6. Look at the map on page 7. Where would you find fossils of ancient sea animals? *(In the area today that was once the Western Interior Seaway.)*

Reteaching the Novice

Have students go to the library and research their fossils. Where did the organism once live? Ask students to locate the place(s) on a map. What present-day organisms are related to their fossils? Encourage students to write a short paragraph, describing the type of climate and environment in which the fossil lived.

Have students compare the fossil puzzle models in Part Two with the illustration on pages 8–9. Explain that fossils are usually parts of an organism; scientists usually have to piece together the fossil information.

Integrating Your Curriculum

INTEGRATING SCIENCE AND ART

3-D Dinosaurs

CHALLENGE · CHALLENGE

Students can find out more about dinosaurs by using modeling clay to create three-dimensional models of them.

Materials for groups of four: 227 g (8 oz: two 4-oz bars) modeling clay, small objects (bottle caps, pebbles, toothpicks, pipe cleaners, buttons, ribbon, and so on), shoebox, scissors, construction paper, markers or crayons

Encourage students to do some research beforehand to find out about the habitat of the dinosaur and its physical characteristics. How long and thick should the tail be? How thick are its limbs? How big is the head? Should the dinosaur have a long, pointed snout or a stubby one? Should it have a big jaw and big teeth? Did dinosaurs have fingers and toes? What was the texture of its skin like?

Students can texture and make features for their dinosaurs with the small objects.

Have them create a habitat for their dinosaurs, using a shoebox. Were there many plants during the age of dinosaurs? Encourage them to illustrate the environment.

CONNECTING TO LIFE SCIENCE

Locating Fossils in Time and Space

SCHOLASTIC NETWORK

Have students find out what the most common types of fossils are in different parts of North America. Assign students different regions (Northeast, Southeast, Midwest, Southwest, and Northwest) and tell them to write a short paragraph about the time period the organisms existed, and about the climate and landforms during those times. Ask students to make a drawing of the fossil. Have them share their findings with the class.

You may want to have students get on-line to share data and ideas about their fossils.

INTEGRATING SOCIAL STUDIES AND LANGUAGE ARTS

Our Ancient Ancestors

Homework Option

The earliest known remains of humans have been found in eastern Africa. It's no wonder that Africa has been called the "birthplace of the human race." Ask students to research a specific site in Africa where early human fossils and bones were found. How old are the fossils and bones that were found on that site? What country(ies) today is a part of that region? Not much is known about how our ancient ancestors lived, but encourage students to research and write about the cultures that live in the area today.

CURIOSITY PLACE

Scientists have found fossilized impressions of dinosaur skin! It's thick and scaly like the skin of a crocodile.

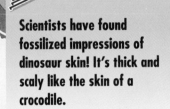

How Do Fossils Form?

LESSON 3

Lesson Road Map

In the last lesson: Students explored how fossils tell us about the past.

In this lesson: Students observe how fossils form. In Part One they observe the process of sedimentation by making a model of a fossil. In Part Two they observe how fossils can be preserved in amber.

In the next lesson: Students will investigate two methods for dating fossils—examining rock layers and radioactive dating.

The Story Line

Grade Level Concept
Different species have inhabited the earth at different times.

Subconcepts
Fossils provide evidence that many species that once inhabited the earth have become extinct.

Changes in the environment or human intervention can result in changes in the characteristics of a population, which are passed on to succeeding generations.

Variation and natural selection have resulted in the evolution of new species.

Lesson Concept
Fossils form when sediments cover organisms or their imprints and harden into rock, or become enclosed in other natural substances.

Getting Organized

This lesson requires one 50-minute session and one 45-minute session. Both Explorations require waiting time.

Materials per Group:
Margarine tub
Petroleum jelly
Water
2 container cups
Tablespoon
Plaster
Powdered potter's clay

Materials per Group:
Petroleum jelly
Mucilage (amber-colored glue)
Small paper cup
Dried bee

PART ONE

Advance Preparation:
In addition to the materials on the clipboard, you'll need sand; large and small leaves, feathers, shells, or other thin objects. You may want to prepare the mixtures for step 2 ahead of time. Also, have the fossils from Lesson 2 handy.

PART TWO

Advance Preparation:
Gather materials.

ALSO FOR THIS LESSON:

ThinkMat 3

Thinking activity about the lesson

LabMats 3A and 3B

Recording sheets for the Explorations

Pages 15–18 and 29–42

Content Background

For a fossil to form, a dead organism or its skeletal remains must be quickly buried so that its remains will not be destroyed by weathering. Then the remains must be left undisturbed during the long process of fossilization. But many factors interfere with fossilization: warm temperatures and exposure to the air may cause the remains to decay too quickly; scavenging animals may disturb the remains; geological changes such as earthquakes may interrupt the process.

Most fossils are formed when an organism's remains are buried in fine layers of sediment, a process known as sedimentation. The soft tissue usually decays quickly, leaving only the hard parts of the organism to be preserved. As the sediment piles up, the pressure of the new layers turns the lower layers to rock. The dead organism's remains may be preserved intact, as a mineralized replica (similar to a mold, in which dissolved minerals have replaced the organic tissues and then hardened), or as an imprint in the rock.

You might also find fossils preserved in amber, which essentially is hardened tree sap. An insect may have become trapped in the sticky sap, which later hardened, encasing the insect. Other fossils are found in tar beds, which were often covered by water. When animals came to drink, they would become mired in the tar. Eventually the animals starved to death, and the tar preserved their remains from decay.

As you'll discover after reading about the "Iceman" in this lesson, ice can also be a great preserver. The Iceman's body was preserved by the low temperatures of the glacial ice and protected by the snow in the rocky hollow.

Vocabulary

sedimentation: A fossil-forming process in which organisms or their traces are covered by layers of mud or sand.

Theme Connection: Patterns of Change

Just as fossils can be preserved, they can also be disrupted by climatic changes and human activities. The earth's atmosphere can also be affected by both natural and human activities, such as volcanic eruptions and industrial pollution.

Considering Second-Language Learners

Have students share their experiences about things they've lost and found. Make sure they know the present and past tenses of the verbs *to lose* and *to find*. After studying the lesson, create a game of Lost and Found. Write the following words on the chalkboard:

Lost and Found

What?

When?

Where?

How?

Afterward, have each student write the name of a type of fossil mentioned in this lesson on a small piece of paper. Fold the pieces and put them in a box. Have each student draw a "fossil" from the box. Ask students to explain "what" type of fossil it is, "when" it was buried, "where" it was found, and "how" it was preserved.

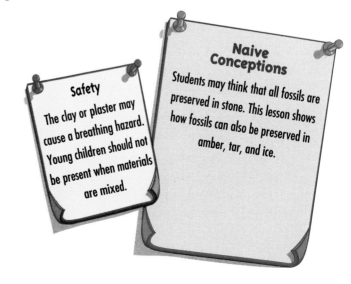

Safety
The clay or plaster may cause a breathing hazard. Young children should not be present when materials are mixed.

Naive Conceptions
Students may think that all fossils are preserved in stone. This lesson shows how fossils can also be preserved in amber, tar, and ice.

What do we know?
What do we want to know?

1

ACTIVATE

EXPLORATION:
Make a fossil with clay and sand.

Process Skills and Objectives

Students will:

- **make models** of fossils from clay and sand

- **observe** how the soft and hard parts of organisms fossilize

- **compare** the fossils they make with the objects they used to make the fossils

- **communicate** that fossils are formed through changes in once-living organisms and their surroundings

Opening the Discussion

Let students read the first paragraph on page 10. Then show them one of the fossils used in Lesson 2. Allow students to feel and describe the texture of the fossil.

Ask: **What material do you think the fossil is made of?** *(They'll probably say rock.)* **How do you think the fossil was formed?** *(Students will probably associate their fossils with rock and soil, and realize that it was formed in the ground.)* Write students' ideas on the Recording Board.

PREPARING FOR THE EXPLORATION

Materials per Group: margarine tub, petroleum jelly, water, 2 container cups, tablespoon, plaster, powdered potter's clay, sand, large and small leaves, feathers, shells, or other thin objects

Suggested Grouping: four

Approximate Time: 30 minutes

Classroom Management: Copy LabMat 3A. Fossils will take a day or two to dry. See Safety note about mixing materials.

LESSON 3

How Do Fossils Form?

The story of life on Earth is like a book with missing pages. Fossils are important clues to those pages, and there's a new fossil discovery almost every month. A college student in Texas comes across the largest dinosaur skull ever found, or a paleontologist finds 100,000-year-old pollen frozen in ice. Living organisms are so fragile that it's a wonder anything is preserved after so many years. Just how do fossils form?

Exploration:
Make a fossil with clay and sand.

You need:
Margarine tub
Petroleum jelly
Water
2 cups
Tablespoon
Plaster
Powdered potter's clay
Sand
Leaves

❶ Rub petroleum jelly over the inside of a margarine tub. Put 1 cm of water in the tub.

❷ Mix 1 spoon of plaster and 3 spoons of clay in one cup. Mix 1 spoon of plaster and 3 spoons of sand in the other cup.

❸ Sprinkle one spoonful of the plaster–clay mixture into the margarine tub. Wait two minutes until it settles. Repeat with the plaster–sand mixture. Repeat again with the plaster–clay mixture.

❹ Cover the three layers with one large leaf or several small leaves. Repeat step 3. Then set the tub aside to dry.

❺ Pop the plaster from the mold and carefully pry it open.

Interpret your results.

- Did the harder or softer parts of the leaf come through more clearly in the fossil? What caused the difference?

- Many fossils are organisms—or their traces—that were covered by layers of mud or sand during <u>sedimentation</u>. Over millions of years, this sediment becomes rock. How is the way you made your fossil like this process? How is it different?

10 SUBCONCEPT ONE: FOSSILS AND EXTINCT SPECIES

EXPLORATION:
Make a fossil with clay and sand.

❶❷ Make sure students layer the mixtures evenly and wait for each layer to settle before adding the next mixture. (The fossil mixture will take a day to dry.) Distribute LabMat 3A.

❸ Ask: **What do you think the layers of clay and sand represent?** *(They represent layers of sediment.)*

❹❺ It'll be easier to split open the layers if there's as little space as possible around the imprinting object.

Troubleshooting: When removing the fossils, have students turn the container upside down and gently press the bottom. Squeezing the container may cause the layers to crumble.

Interpret Your Results

- The hard parts of the object should be the most clearly visible in the fossil because they aren't crushed by the layers of clay and sand.

- The activity is like the process of sedimentation because the object is sandwiched between layers of sediment that then hardened and preserved the object's imprint. The activity differs from sedimentation because it takes only a few minutes for the layers to harden instead of millions of years.

Exploration Connection:
Using reference books

Have you ever found something you never expected to see again—a ball lost in the bushes or a sled buried in the snow all winter long?

Imagine how two Germans hiking in the Italian Alps in 1991 felt when they saw a head sticking out of snow. Helmut and Erika Simon thought the person was an accident victim. They didn't know the accident had taken place 5,000 years earlier.

The victim, a man with dark wavy hair, was between 25 and 40 years old. He may have been a shepherd, and he was probably exhausted from climbing the mountain pass. He lay down out of the wind in a hollow in the rock. His grass cape and straw-stuffed boots didn't keep him warm enough. Overcome by the cold, he was buried in an airtight pocket of snow.

A glacier moved slowly above him for thousands of years but did not move him. Nearby were his copper ax, a bow and arrows, a backpack filled with berries and meat, and a flint knife. The Iceman of the Alps is one of the oldest and best-preserved prehistoric human beings ever found.

What do you think made it possible for the Iceman to stay so well preserved for 5,000 years? What problems do you think paleontologists have as they study the Iceman and try to keep him preserved.

To find out about other surprise fossil finds, turn to pages 15–18 and 29–42 of *Dinosaurs Walked Here*.

Exploration Connection:
Using reference books

After students have read the Exploration Connection, explain to them how the cold temperatures and the lack of exposure to the air helped preserve the Iceman. Today the Iceman's body is being preserved in a refrigerator. Scientists must constantly make sure that the refrigerator temperatures are cold enough to prevent decay.

In *Dinosaurs Walked Here* there are detailed descriptions of how animals may have become trapped in the La Brea tar pits in Los Angeles. Ask: **Can you name other natural substances that could entrap animals?** *(Answers may vary, but might include ice, quicksand, lava, flood waters, and so on.)*

▼ The Iceman of the Alps and his belongings

11

EXPLORATION:
Make a see-through fossil.

Process Skills and Objectives

Students will:

- **make models** that resemble amber fossils

- **observe** that fossils can also form through preservation in amber as well as in other natural substances

---

- **compare** the similarities and differences between the process of fossilization in amber and in their models

---

- **predict** ways in which animals and plants could become trapped in amber

---

- **communicate** the similarities in all the fossilization processes they've learned about

---

PREPARING FOR THE EXPLORATION

Materials per Group: petroleum jelly, mucilage (amber-colored glue), small paper cup, dried bee

Suggested Grouping: four

Approximate Time: 30 minutes

Classroom Management: Copy LabMat 3B. Do one of the Options during the week that the fossil model is drying to keep the lesson fresh in students' minds.

EXPLORATION:
Make a see-through fossil.

❶ ❷ Have students predict whether the bee will decay, dissolve, or be preserved. Ask them to give reasons to support their predictions. Distribute LabMat 3B.

Student Pages 12–13

❸ ❹ Make sure students handle the dead bees carefully so they remain intact.

❺ ❻ Ask: **How is this process like the other fossilization processes you've learned about?** *(In all the processes, an organism is covered by a substance that preserves it in some way.)*

---

3 How Do Fossils Form?

Not all fossils are preserved in rock or ice. Tar can trap and preserve plants and animals as fossils, too. So can other natural substances. Some fossils of insects look as if they could fly or scuttle off in a second. But they haven't moved for millions of years.

Exploration:
Make a see-through fossil.

You need:
Petroleum jelly
Mucilage
Small paper cup
Dried bee

❶ Use your finger to coat the inside of the paper cup with petroleum jelly.

❷ Pour mucilage into the paper cup until the cup is one-quarter full.

❸ Drop the dried bee into the mucilage.

❹ Now pour a little more mucilage into your cup—just enough to cover the bee.

❺ Put your cup in a safe place for a week, but don't cover it. Try not to peek before it's ready.

❻ When the week is up, pop your fossil out of the cup.

Interpret your results.

- What happened to the mucilage during the week? What does the bee look like now?

- Sap from trees sometimes hardens into a clear substance called amber. How is the mucilage in this activity like amber?

- How do you think an animal or a plant could have become trapped in amber? Imagine a scene millions of years ago in which an insect was trapped in sap that became amber. Describe the scene.

- What would have happened to the same insect or plant if it had been trapped in mud?

12

Interpret Your Results

- The mucilage hardened. The bee may look a little waterlogged but otherwise unchanged.

- Like amber, the mucilage hardens into a partly clear solid substance, which doesn't dissolve in water.

- Encourage a variety of scenarios, such as an insect mistaking the sap on a tree branch for blood.

- It might have formed a sedimentary fossil.

Closer to Home: Telltale footprints

Have students discuss the different types of animal footprints they've seen in the woods, on the beach, in the desert, in the park, and so on. Ask: **What did you learn about the animal from its footprints?** *(Answers will vary, but students were probably able to identify the type of animal that made the imprint, the size of the animal, and the direction the animal was heading.)*

- The dinosaur tracks are all pointed in the same direction. They may have traveled in groups. The ground was probably muddy.

- A meat-eating dinosaur might have been stalking a plant-eating dinosaur.

- The meat-eating dinosaur's tracks would probably continue alone because the plant-eater would be lying dead after the meat-eater caught up with it.

This is a good time to distribute ThinkMat 3.

▲ This photo shows the fossilized tracks of five dinosaurs of the same kind.

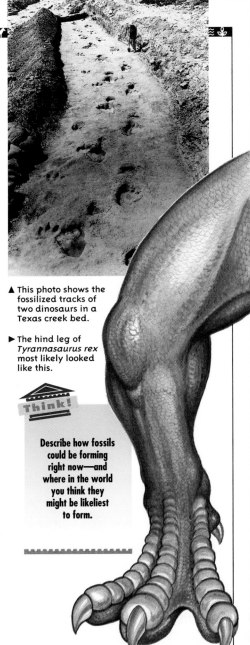

▲ This photo shows the fossilized tracks of two dinosaurs in a Texas creek bed.

▶ The hind leg of *Tyrannasaurus rex* most likely looked like this.

Closer to Home: Telltale footprints

If you've ever walked barefoot across a muddy field, you know how to recognize your own footprints. Paleontologists recognize footprints, too. They learn a lot about the past by studying footprints of animals that have been dead for millions of years.

- How can you tell that the five plant-eating dinosaurs in the photo above were walking in the same direction? What can you say about the way this kind of dinosaur might have lived? What do you think the ground was like where they walked?

- In the photo on the upper right, the plant-eating dinosaurs left round tracks; the meat-eating dinosaurs had claws and left claw-toed prints. What do you think might have been happening in that creek bed?

- If one set of tracks suddenly stopped, would you expect the other tracks to belong to the plant-eating dinosaur or the meat-eating dinosaur? Why?

Think!

Describe how fossils could be forming right now—and where in the world you think they might be likeliest to form.

Think!

The likeliest places for fossilization include the bottom of a lake or ocean where sediment is deposited; high mountains where year-round glaciers might preserve remains; or forests where amber might form.

LESSON THINKING SKILLS:
Recognizing Cause and Effect; Formulating Hypotheses

SUBCONCEPT ONE: FOSSILS AND EXTINCT SPECIES   **13**

Assessment Options

Using Students' Process Performance and Recorded Observations

Written Options

1. Students' responses on their LabMats and ThinkMat should give you a clear idea of their understanding of the lesson concept. Use Student Benchmarks to analyze their answers.

2. Have students make a list noting the similarities and differences between the two fossil models they made in the lesson.

Student Benchmarks

Proficient: Students discuss the process of fossilization in sediment, ice, and amber, and can identify the parts of fossils that preserve best.

Apprentice: Students demonstrate how their fossil models are similar to real-life fossils found in sediments and amber.

Novice: Students know that fossils form in natural substances, but may not be able to identify the processes.

Portfolio

Students may decide they want to include the LabMats from this lesson in their Portfolio. In addition, they may want to include one of the Options.

Oral Options

Listen to students as they do the Explorations. Student Benchmarks will give you an idea of how well they understand the lesson concept.

1. In Part One, ask students which part of an organism will fossilize the best—the soft part or the hard part. How would exposure to elements such as rain and snow affect their models? Explain that similar to sedimentation some erosion would take place over a period of time.

2. In Part Two, ask students to compare the see-through fossil with the clay fossil. Where would they most likely find each type of fossil?

3. How students answer the Think and Closer to Home questions will also give you a good idea of their understanding of the lesson concept.

The following questions can also be used to assess understanding of the lesson concept:

4. What could people in the future discover from fossils of animals that are living today? *(Accept all reasonable answers. For example, fossils can give clues to where oceans once existed.)*

5. What type of natural disturbances might interfere with fossil formation? *(Natural activities such as earthquakes, volcanic eruptions, tornadoes, and so on.)*

Reteaching the Novice

Have students reexamine their clay and mucilage fossils. Ask them to explain how the clay and mucilage are like sediment and amber. How are they different? What type of conditions are necessary for fossils to form in sediment and amber? In what environments would you find these types of fossils? How do these two processes differ?

To help students better understand the fossilization processes, discuss how they layered clay and sand in the first Exploration and poured mucilage in the second Exploration.

Integrating Your Curriculum

INTEGRATING GEOGRAPHY AND ART

Finding Out About Amber

CHALLENGE · CHALLENGE

Amber is tree sap that hardened with exposure to air and with pressure when a tree was buried or ended up under water. Specimens in amber—sometimes from trees that are now extinct—may be as much as 40 million years old. Sometimes specimens of once-living organisms have been preserved whole in amber. Have students research the regions of the world where amber is abundant. Ask them to select one country. Then have them research and write a paragraph about the type of amber found in that country and how it might be used. Have a map available so students can locate their regions.

LONG–TERM CLASS PROJECT

Remains to Be Seen

Have students investigate what can happen to the remains of organisms that are buried in the ground. Do they get eaten by animals, decay completely, or leave remains that could become fossils?

Materials: shovel; ruler; objects such as a chicken wing with the meat still on it, an orange, a handful of berries, a raw egg, a leaf, a feather, a seashell, a wooden block, a ham or beef bone, a piece of thick cotton rope, and a piece of leather; wooden sticks; marker (metal cans and soil if you're doing the activity indoors)

Bury each object in its own hole about 10 cm (4 in.) deep, cover it with damp earth, and mark the spot.

Check on the remains after two weeks, four weeks, and six weeks. Have students record their observations.

CONNECTING TO LIFE SCIENCE

Finding Fossils

Homework Option

Most fossils are found in sedimentary rock such as limestone, which is commonly used as a building material. So even though students may not live near a fossil bed, they can hunt for fossils in the sedimentary rock found in the outside walls of buildings (embedded in brick, cement, and so on), sidewalks, stone floors, and other places. Have students look for fossils in their area. Ask them to write a paragraph about the fossils, including where a fossil was found and what type of organism it might have been. Encourage students to make a sketch of each fossil.

CURIOSITY PLACE

A fossil of the largest flying reptile ever found, a pterosaur, shows that this animal had a wingspan of 12 m (39 ft)—larger than that of a small airplane.

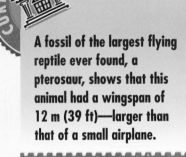

How Can You Decide Which Fossils Are Older?

Student Pages 14–17

Lesson Road Map

In the last lesson: Students observed how fossils form.

In this lesson: Students investigate two methods for dating fossils—examining rock layers and radioactive dating.

In the next lesson: Students will discover how fossils help to tell the earth's history.

Getting Organized

This lesson requires one 50-minute session.

Materials per Group:
ThinkMat 4
Scissors

Advance Preparation:
Copy both sides of ThinkMat 4 and cut apart the sections of rock layers on each copy for each group.

The Story Line

Grade Level Concept
Different species have inhabited the earth at different times.

Subconcepts
Fossils provide evidence that many species that once inhabited the earth have become extinct.

Changes in the environment or human intervention can result in changes in the characteristics of a population, which are passed on to succeeding generations.

Variation and natural selection have resulted in the evolution of new species.

Lesson Concept
A fossil's age can be determined by studying the rock layers above and below it, and by radioactive dating.

ALSO FOR THIS LESSON:

ThinkMat 4

For use with the Exploration

LabMat 4

Recording sheet for the Exploration

Pages 21–26

Content Background

One way to date a fossil is to examine the rock layer in which the fossil was found. Most fossils are found in sedimentary rock. This type of rock generally forms as sediment is deposited in horizontal layers at the bottom of a body of water. If the layers haven't been disturbed by excavations or natural activities, scientists usually assume that older rock will be found in the lower layers and younger rock in the upper layers. By examining the position of the rock layer in which a fossil was found, scientists can determine the layer's "relative age"—whether that rock layer is older or younger than other rock layers. To determine "absolute age"—the actual age—other methods must be used.

To find the absolute age of fossils, scientists use carbon-14 dating. Carbon-14 is a radioactive form of carbon found in certain molecules in the atmosphere. Plants take in small amounts of carbon-14 from the carbon dioxide in the air, and animals absorb it when they eat plants. Living organisms also contain another form of carbon, carbon-12, which is stable. At the time of death, organisms contain both carbon-14 and carbon-12 in a definite proportion. But after death, organisms no longer absorb carbon. In fact, the radioactive carbon-14 in their cells starts to break down into nitrogen, while the quantity of carbon-12 stays the same. It takes 5,730 years for one half of the carbon-14 in a fossil to break down radioactively. By comparing the quantity of carbon-14 in a fossil with the quantity of carbon-12, scientists can determine how long ago the fossil organism died. Scientists have found that over time the levels of carbon-14 in the atmosphere have varied, but not enough to affect the accuracy of carbon-14 dates significantly.

Vocabulary

geological period: A period of time on the earth with specific climates, geological formations, and forms of life.

radioactive dating: Measurement of age by the amount of change in a radioactive element in a fossil.

Theme Connection: Patterns of Change

By knowing the rate at which carbon-14 decays, scientists can estimate the age of fossils and learn how living organisms have changed over time. Similarly, scientists can also learn about past climates using carbon-14 technique as well as examining tree growth rings.

Considering Second-Language Learners

Help students construct comparative sentences related to the lesson concept, using the following terms: *old, older, oldest* and *young, younger, youngest*. Ask students to look at the pictures in their books. You might also want to bring in newspapers or magazines that show people of different ages. Direct students' attention to the pictures and ask them to describe what they see using the above-mentioned adjectives. Depending on their level of proficiency, ask simple questions to elicit more specific descriptions.

If time allows, continue this exercise with other combinations of adjectives, such as *long, longer, longest*.

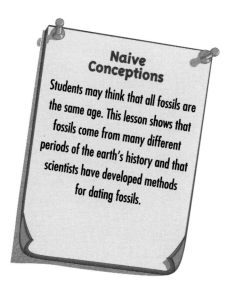

Naive Conceptions

Students may think that all fossils are the same age. This lesson shows that fossils come from many different periods of the earth's history and that scientists have developed methods for dating fossils.

LESSON 4

What do we know?
What do we want to know?

1

ACTIVATE

EXPLORATION:
Watch time fly in the Grand Canyon.

Process Skills and Objectives

Students will:

- **observe** that some fossils are older than others

- **compare** the layers of rock on their ThinkMat

- **predict** the types of fossils that can be found at different elevations of the canyon wall

Opening the Discussion

Have students think about the way they may pile their clothes onto a chair or other piece of furniture. How high does the pile get before they start putting away those clothes?

Ask: **Where are the clothes that you wore early in the week?** *(They're at the bottom or near the bottom of the pile.)* **How about the clothes you wore yesterday?** *(They're at the top.)*

Have students read the introductory paragraph on page 14. Write down their responses to the question in the text on the Recording Board.

PREPARING FOR THE EXPLORATION

Materials per Group: ThinkMat 4, scissors

Suggested Grouping: four

Approximate Time: 20 minutes

Classroom Management: Copy ThinkMat 4 and LabMat 4. There are several ways that the layers can be arranged. After students have experimented with their layers, have each group display a different example.

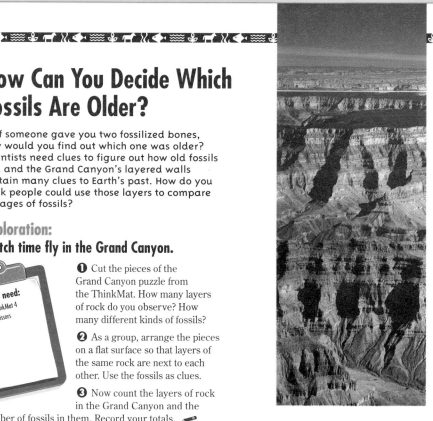

LESSON 4

How Can You Decide Which Fossils Are Older?

If someone gave you two fossilized bones, how would you find out which one was older? Scientists need clues to figure out how old fossils are, and the Grand Canyon's layered walls contain many clues to Earth's past. How do you think people could use those layers to compare the ages of fossils?

Exploration:
Watch time fly in the Grand Canyon.

You need:
ThinkMat 4
Scissors

❶ Cut the pieces of the Grand Canyon puzzle from the ThinkMat. How many layers of rock do you observe? How many different kinds of fossils?

❷ As a group, arrange the pieces on a flat surface so that layers of the same rock are next to each other. Use the fossils as clues.

❸ Now count the layers of rock in the Grand Canyon and the number of fossils in them. Record your totals.

Interpret your results.

- What clue helped you to figure out which was the topmost layer exposed in the canyon?

- You can see two billion years of time in the layers of the Grand Canyon wall. Based on your observations of rock layers and fossils, which layers of the canyon wall would you say were formed first, those at the top or those at the bottom?

- In general, would you expect fossils to be older or younger the deeper into the canyon you go? Why?

Student Pages 14–15

14

EXPLORATION:
Watch time fly in the Grand Canyon.

❶ Distribute ThinkMat 4 and LabMat 4. Make sure each group has all the sections of the rock layers.

🌀 **Troubleshooting:** Allow students to work on the floor or arrange desks or tables so that they have room to lay out the rock sections side by side.

❷ By matching the fossils, students will be able to arrange the layers in proper order.

❸ Ask students: **Which layer has the oldest fossils?** *(the bottom layer)* **Which layer has the most recent fossils?** *(the top layer)* Encourage students to examine other groups' arrangements of rock layers. The horizontal arrangement of layers may vary (one group may have a mesa where another group has a canyon), but the vertical order of the layers remains the same as long as similar layers have been matched.

▲ As the Colorado River carved out the Grand Canyon, it revealed layers of sedimentary rock built up over 2 billion years.

LAYERS OF TIME IN THE GRAND CANYON

Geological Period	Elevation above sea level
	2622 m Canyon rim
Permian	
	2000 m
Carboniferous	
	1500 m
Devonian	
Cambrian	1000 m
	500 m
Pre-cambrian	366 m Canyon floor
	0

Interpret Your Results

• The flowers and trees growing from the soil indicate the topmost layer of the canyon.

• Because sedimentary rock forms in layers, the layers at the bottom were formed first.

• In general, the deeper the rock layer, the older it is; so fossils found in deeper layers would also be older. Likewise, the closer to the surface a fossil is, the more recently it was alive.

Exploration Connection:
Using reference books

From the diagram of the Grand Canyon, students will see that the trilobite (Cambrian period) from Lesson 2 is closest to the canyon floor. The petrified wood (Cretaceous period) is younger than the youngest rocks of the canyon.

After students have read the selection in *Dinosaurs Walked Here,* ask: **What fossilized the trees in Yellowstone Park?** *(Volcanic eruptions buried the trees in ash and rock.)* **What did scientists learn from the fossilized trees?** *((At one time the climate was much warmer in that area.))*

Exploration Connection:
Using reference books

The Grand Canyon is so old that the only fossils in its oldest layers are microscopic organisms. These organisms were the only living things on Earth until about 650 million years ago. Then, the number of species on Earth began to change—in a big way.

As you walk up from the bottom of the canyon, you can find fossils of hundreds of different plants and animals that lived at different times—or geological periods—in Earth's history.

Look at the diagram above. Which of the fossilized plants or animals you studied in Lesson 2 belongs to the period closest to the canyon floor? Which of your fossils is younger than the youngest rocks of the Grand Canyon?

Sedimentary rock is not the only keeper of Earth's early history. In Yellowstone National Park, ancient tropical plants were preserved beneath the surface in a different way. Read pages 21–26 in *Dinosaurs Walked Here* to find out how.

SUBCONCEPT ONE: FOSSILS AND EXTINCT SPECIES 15

Closer to Home: Clocks without hands

After students have read the text, explain to them that all living organisms also contain carbon-12. At the time of death, organisms have a definite proportion of carbon-14 and carbon-12. The carbon-14 starts to break down into nitrogen while the carbon-12 remains the same.

Ask students: **How are the methods for dating fossils in this section different from dating fossils in rock layers?** *(Help students realize that rock layers give the relative age while radioactive dating and ice-core sampling give the exact age.)*

- Uranium dating would be used because the other methods don't go back far enough.

- Thermal drills, or "hot pipes," would be used.

- The bone is 11,460 years old.

---

4   How Can You Decide Which Fossils Are Older?

Closer to Home: Clocks without hands

If you've ever gone to the beach—or an Italian restaurant—you've probably had a chance to look at a clamshell. You may have noticed the ridges on the outside of the shell. But did you know these ridges are a kind of clock? They appear as the shell grows, so the more ridges, the older the shell.

Nature is full of things that measure time in one way or another, and paleontologists use some of them to figure out how old fossils are. The most common way to find out the age of a fossil involves <u>radioactive dating</u>, or measuring time by the amount of change in a radioactive element called carbon-14.

Scientists date fossils that are 70,000 years old or less by measuring how much carbon-14 they still contain. All living things contain carbon-14, a radioactive material that slowly breaks down. It takes 5,730 years for half the carbon-14 in a fossil to break down. Scientists call this period of time the half-life of carbon-14, as half of the radioactive atoms have broken down. Other radioactive elements, such as certain forms of uranium, are used to date rocks that are billions of years old. The methods are similar to those used for carbon-14 dating.

▲ 12,000 years ago: The living tree contains carbon-14.

Scientists also use ice core samples to study the earth's history. Hollow thermal drills called hot pipes remove long cylinders of ice from the ground. Scientists then count the thin layers to see how many years the ice has been piling up. They use clues found in the ice—pollen grains, mineral dust, volcanic ash, and air bubbles—to learn about conditions as far back as 150,000 years ago.

- What method would you use to date the Grand Canyon fossils from this lesson's ThinkMat?

- What method would you use to find out about volcanic activity in Antarctica?

- What is the age of a bone that contains half as much carbon-14 as a 5,730-year-old fossil?

▲ The ridges on a clamshell reveal its age.

Diverse perspectives

According to the fossil record, animals and plants lived in and near the Grand Canyon area millions of years ago. During the past 4,000 years different Native-American tribes have lived in the canyon. Archaeologists have found over 500 sites of ancient Indian pueblos around the rim of the canyon. They've also found cliff dwellings in its lower walls.

Several Native-American nations live in the Grand Canyon area today. One tribe, the Havasupai, is a small community of about 200 people. They earn a living by selling goods to tourists visiting the Grand Canyon and by farming on the canyon floor.

This is a good opportunity to have students get on-line to share ideas about dating methods.

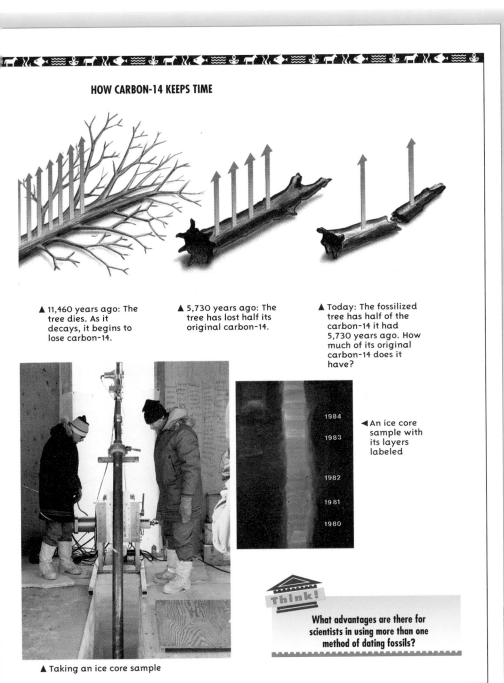

HOW CARBON-14 KEEPS TIME

▲ 11,460 years ago: The tree dies. As it decays, it begins to lose carbon-14.

▲ 5,730 years ago: The tree has lost half its original carbon-14.

▲ Today: The fossilized tree has half of the carbon-14 it had 5,730 years ago. How much of its original carbon-14 does it have?

◄ An ice core sample with its layers labeled

▲ Taking an ice core sample

Think!

What advantages are there for scientists in using more than one method of dating fossils?

Think!

Ask students to review all the dating methods they've learned about. Using more than one dating method would help scientists verify the age of a fossil.

LESSON THINKING SKILLS:
Recognizing Cause and Effect: Drawing Conclusions

17

Assessment Options

Using Students' Process Performance and Recorded Observations

Written Options

1. Students' responses on their LabMat and ThinkMat should give you a clear idea of their understanding of the lesson concept. Use Student Benchmarks to analyze their answers.

2. Using the results of their Exploration, have students write a short descriptive paragraph about the rock layers of the Grand Canyon.

Student Benchmarks

Proficient: Students discuss and identify the dating methods used to find the relative age and the absolute age of fossils.

Apprentice: Students demonstrate how the age of rock layers can help determine the relative age of fossils.

Novice: Students discuss how the oldest rock layers are usually located at the bottom, but may not understand the concept of relative dating.

Portfolio

Students may decide they want to include the LabMat from this lesson in their Portfolio. They also may want to include their paragraphs from the Written Option.

Oral Options

Listen to students as they do the Exploration. Student Benchmarks will give you an idea of how well they understand the lesson concept.

1. Ask students how they're comparing the rock layers to one another. Can they tell which fossils are older from the order of the rock layers?

2. How students answer the Exploration Connection and Think questions will also give you a good idea of their understanding of the lesson concept.

The following questions can also be used to assess understanding of the lesson concept:

3. Is it more meaningful to understand when events occurred in history relative to other events or to know the exact dates of historical events? *(Exact dates of historical events help to place these events more accurately in time, while general time relationships between events enable you to learn about the causes that may have influenced those events.)*

4. Scientists have found that the levels of carbon-14 in the atmosphere have varied over time. How might these fluctuations affect carbon-14 dating? *(It could affect the accuracy of carbon-14 dates.)*

5. Where would scientists use thermal drills? *(Thermal drills are used in regions layered with ice, such as the Arctic.)*

Reteaching the Novice

Display the different ways that students composed the rock layers from the Exploration. You may also want to bring in photographs or diagrams of earth strata from science reference books or magazines (mesas, buttes, canyons, sea cliffs, mountainsides). Ask students if the oldest layers are always at the bottom. What could upset the order of the earth strata? Can the exact age of a fossil be determined by the rock layer it was found in? Why or why not?

Integrating Your Curriculum

CONNECTING TO LIFE SCIENCE

Layers of Time

CHALLENGE · CHALLENGE ·

The earth's layers may not always end up in chronological order. Earthquakes and volcanic eruptions can shift the earth and its fossil records.

Materials for group of four: 1.5 kg (3 lb) of modeling clay (3 different colors; approximately 500 g [1 lb] for each color), small objects (leaves, twigs, feathers, chicken bones, egg shells, toothpicks; for the best results, use both thin and thick objects)

Have students make a 10 cm × 13 cm (4" × 5") rectangular layer (2.5 cm thick) with each color clay so that they'll have three layers of different colors.

- On the first layer, have students place some objects in the clay. Then have them cover the first layer with another color of clay and press down on the second layer.

- Repeat the process for the second layer.

- The third layer, the top, won't have any objects placed on it.

Once the layers are complete, have students slowly remove each layer.

- Ask students to write down their observations about the type of mark or trace each object left, if any at all.

INTEGRATING SOCIAL STUDIES AND LANGUAGE ARTS

Fossil Sites

Early human fossils have been discovered around the world. Some major human fossil sites are located in Asia (Choukoutien, Lantian), Africa (Olduvai Gorge, Koobi Fora, Lothagam, Ternifine, Taung), Europe (Swanscombe, Neander Valley, Terre Amata), and Australia (Lake Mungo). Review some of the locations with students and ask them to select one site to research. Ask them to write a few paragraphs about what was discovered at the site. How old are the fossils or bones found there? From what was found on the site, could scientists figure out how the early humans lived? Were tools or pottery found on the site?

USING THE LIBRARY

A Day in the Life of a Paleontologist

Homework Option

Ask students to research the job of a paleontologist. Have them find out the type of skills and tools needed for an excavation. Then tell students to imagine that they are paleontologists. Have them write a paragraph describing the steps of identifying a site, painstakingly uncovering the fossil, studying and recording its location, preparing it for removal, removing and transporting it, and cleaning it. Encourage students to draw pictures of excavation tools to accompany their writing.

CURIOSITY PLACE

Scientists even study ancient air! By analyzing air bubbles 3,048 m (10,000 ft) deep in glaciers, they can find out what the earth's atmosphere was like 250,000 years ago.

How Do Fossils Show the History of Earth's Species?

Student Pages 18-21

Lesson Road Map

In the last lesson: Students investigated two methods for dating fossils—examining rock layers and radioactive dating.

In this lesson: Students discover how fossils help to tell Earth's history. In Part One they make a time line of Earth's history. In Part Two they locate where certain fossils belong.

In the next lesson: Students will evaluate several theories about the extinction of the dinosaur.

The Story Line

Grade Level Concept
Different species have inhabited the earth at different times.

Subconcepts
Fossils provide evidence that many species that once inhabited the earth have become extinct.

Changes in the environment or human intervention can result in changes in the characteristics of a population, which are passed on to succeeding generations.

Variation and natural selection have resulted in the evolution of new species.

Lesson Concept
Fossils show that species have appeared on Earth at different times, and that many life forms have become extinct.

Getting Organized

This lesson requires one 50-minute session and one 45-minute session.

Materials per Group:
15-m (50-ft) roll of adding machine paper or newsprint paper
Ruler
Tape
Markers or crayons

PART ONE

Advance Preparation:
In addition to gathering materials, allow time for students to go to the school library to check out reference materials on the different eras of Earth's history. Also keep the fossils from Lesson 2 handy.

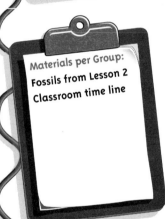

Materials per Group:
Fossils from Lesson 2
Classroom time line

PART TWO

Advance Preparation:
In addition to gathering materials, have the reference materials used in Part One handy.

ALSO FOR THIS LESSON:

ThinkMat 5

Reviewing the subconcept

LabMats 5A and 5B

Recording sheets for the Explorations

Content Background

From fossils, scientists have been able to reconstruct an enormous part of Earth's history—from what extinct animals and plants looked like to the climate and types of environment in which they lived. How do scientists keep all this information in order? Based on studies of fossils in sedimentary rocks around the world, scientists have divided geological time into four eras (which are subdivided into periods and epochs). In each era there are characteristic fossils from which certain evolutionary changes can be traced.

The earliest era is the Precambrian, which lasted from the formation of Earth (about 4.5 billion years ago) to the beginning of the Paleozoic era (about 570 million years ago). Middle Precambrian rocks contain the oldest known fossils. There are traces of bacteria and algae that date to more than three billion years ago. In the next era, the Paleozoic, you'll also find fossils of early plants and animals. This era spans from about 570 million years ago to about 225 million years ago; it's subdivided into the Cambrian, Ordovician, Silurian, Devonian, Carboniferous (Mississippian and Pennsylvanian), and Permian periods. The third era, the Mesozoic, lasted from about 225 million years ago to about 65 million years ago. This era is subdivided into the Triassic, Jurassic, and Cretaceous periods. Rocks from this era contain fossils of more complex organisms (dinosaurs, mammals, reptiles, and birds). The current era, the Cenozoic, began about 65 million years ago. This era is subdivided into the Tertiary period (with Paleocene, Eocene, Oligocene, Miocene, and Pliocene epochs) and the Quaternary period (with Pleistocene and Holocene epochs). Mammal fossils are quite common in rocks of this era, but you won't find human fossils until about 2.4 million years ago.

Teachers' Bookshelf

Eldredge, Niles. *Lifepulse: Episodes From the Story of the Fossil Record.* New York: Facts on File, 1987.

Gould, Stephen Jay. *The Book of Life: An Illustrated History of Life on Earth.* New York: W.W. Norton, 1993.

Theme Connection: Patterns of Change

The fossil record shows that life forms on Earth are constantly changing as species appear and later become extinct. Similarly, Earth's landforms are continually changing as a result of both human development and natural forces such as earthquakes.

Considering Second-Language Learners

Tell students that they're going to make time lines. Ask students to think about important events in their lives. Have them make lists, giving the year in which each event occurred. You may want to suggest birthdays, first day at school, sports contests, and so on. On a sheet of paper, have students draw a line and then place the events in chronological order. Students can also make drawings to accompany the events.

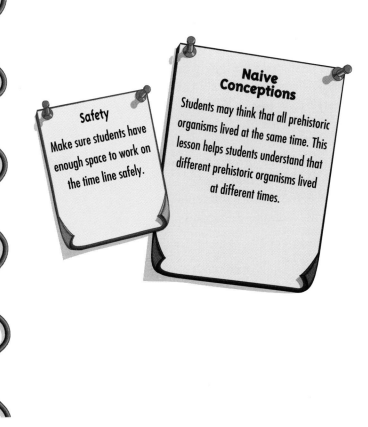

Safety

Make sure students have enough space to work on the time line safely.

Naive Conceptions

Students may think that all prehistoric organisms lived at the same time. This lesson helps students understand that different prehistoric organisms lived at different times.

LESSON 5 **Part One**

What do we know?
What do we want to know?

1

ACTIVATE

EXPLORATION:
Make a time line.

Process Skills and Objectives

Students will:

- **order and measure** information about the history of Earth along the time line

- **compare** the length of different time periods and the number of developments in each period

- **communicate** that various species of plants and animals appeared during the different geological periods

Opening the Discussion

Have students read the first paragraph on page 18. Show students one of the fossils used in Lesson 2. Ask students: **Does this fossil tell you anything about the history of the organism?** (*No, but you might be able to identify the organism.*)

Would fossils from one layer provide enough information about a species' history? (*No; you would need to know about the layers below and above. Not enough information is provided in one layer; each layer has to be placed into a time frame.*) Write down students' responses on the Recording Board.

PREPARING FOR THE EXPLORATION

Materials per Group: 15-m (50-ft) roll of adding machine paper or newsprint paper, ruler, tape, markers or crayons

Suggested Grouping: entire class

Approximate Time: 30 minutes

Classroom Management: Copy LabMat 5A. Since the first Exploration is necessary for the second Exploration, you can't jigsaw this lesson.

LESSON 5

How Do Fossils Show the History of Earth's Species?

The fossil record is like a giant jigsaw puzzle with pieces scattered in every region of the earth. People around the world have found pieces of this puzzle. By fitting the pieces together, they've learned a lot about Earth's life forms and the geological time periods in which they lived. But some of these periods lasted hundreds of millions of years. How can we show how long that is?

Exploration:
Make a time line.

You need:
15 m roll of adding machine paper
Ruler
Tape
Markers or crayons

❶ Tape the end of the paper to a classroom wall so that it can be unrolled to the left.

❷ Stretch the paper along the wall. Tape it in place. At the right-hand end, write "Now."

❸ Draw a vertical line 30 cm to the left of "Now." Label it "100 MYA" (million years ago).

❹ Divide your time line into 30 cm sections. Label each section by adding 100 to the number to the right of it. Label the line at 4,500 MYA "The Beginning of Earth."

❺ Read the time line on the right. Then mark the geological periods on your classroom time line.

❻ Put all the other information that you know about the history of the earth on your classroom time line.

Interpret your results.

- Which is the longest period on your classroom time line? the shortest?

- Why did you have to use measurements of 100 million years on your time line?

- When everyone in class worked on the time line, where did most of the activity take place? Why?

- What do your observations of the time line tell you about life on Earth?

Precambrian
Million years ago
570
Cambrian

18 SUBCONCEPT ONE: FOSSILS AND EXTINCT SPECIES

Student Pages 18–19

EXPLORATION: Make a time line.

❷ Ask students to hold the adding machine paper as you attach it to the wall. Distribute LabMat 5A.

❹ Have students use the time line on pages 18–19 to insert the names of the different periods. Make sure students understand that the Precambrian section of the time line goes further back in time, to about 4.5 billion years ago, when Earth's crust began forming.

❺❻ Supply reference books from the school library so that students can add information about major climate changes, such as ice ages. Ask them to include the appearance of *Homo sapiens*.

🌀 **Troubleshooting:** Suggest that students make comic strip-style balloons to add information.

Interpret Your Results

- The longest period is the Precambrian; the shortest is the Quaternary.

- It's the only way to fit 4.5 billion years on a 15-m (50-ft) time line.

- Most of the activity took place near the "Now" end, because most events that students are studying occurred in the recent past.

- Life has existed on Earth for a long time. Both Earth and the life forms on it have changed a great deal over billions of years.

Exploration Connection:
Interpreting graphs

Time lines are a great way to help you understand the hundreds of millions of years that make up the geological time scale. Looking at a time line is like looking at a picture of time passing.

- Study the time line on the graph below. Which came first, the Age of Fishes or the Age of Dinosaurs?

- During which geological period did amphibians appear? How much later did the first reptiles appear?

- What kinds of plants lived on Earth during the time of the dinosaurs?

- In what period did our ancestors first appear on Earth?

Exploration Connection:
Interpreting graphs

Ask students: **From the illustration on the time line, what can you tell about how the climate changed?** (*Students will see that some periods had lush landforms while other periods had dry and barren areas.*)

- The Age of Fishes came first.

- Amphibians appeared during the Devonian period, and reptiles appeared in the next period (Carboniferous).

- Pine forests covered much of Earth.

- Our ancestors first appeared on Earth during the Quarternary period.

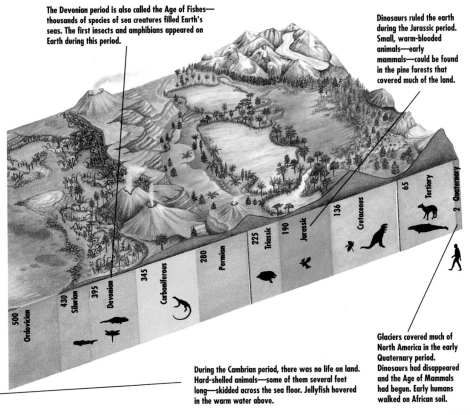

The Devonian period is also called the Age of Fishes—thousands of species of sea creatures filled Earth's seas. The first insects and amphibians appeared on Earth during this period.

Dinosaurs ruled the earth during the Jurassic period. Small, warm-blooded animals—early mammals—could be found in the pine forests that covered much of the land.

500 Ordovician
430 Silurian
395 Devonian
345 Carboniferous
280 Permian
225 Triassic
190 Jurassic
136 Cretaceous
65 Tertiary
2 Quaternary

During the Cambrian period, there was no life on land. Hard-shelled animals—some of them several feet long—skidded across the sea floor. Jellyfish hovered in the warm water above.

Glaciers covered much of North America in the early Quaternary period. Dinosaurs had disappeared and the Age of Mammals had begun. Early humans walked on African soil.

19

EXPLORATION:
Find your fossil in time.

Process Skills and Objectives

Students will:

- **interpret data** about their fossils to place them on the time line

- **order** their fossils on the time line

- **compare** the ages of species by using the time line

PREPARING FOR THE EXPLORATION

Materials per Group: fossils from Lesson 2, classroom time line

Suggested Grouping: eight

Approximate Time: 20 minutes

Classroom Management: Copy LabMat 5B. Have each group member carefully examine the fossil and draw a picture of it.

EXPLORATION:
Find your fossil in time.

❶ ❷ In each kit there are four fossils: a crinoid stem, a brachiopod shell, a trilobite, and a piece of petrified wood. Each fossil will have a label that identifies the period in which the organism lived. Distribute LabMat 5B.

❸ Have a number of reference books from the school library available in the classroom for students to consult. Ask students to draw other plants and animals that existed during the same time as their fossils. Then have students review the caption and maps of Pangaea on pages 20–21. Ask: **What geological period did the formation of Pangaea take place in?** *(From the time line on page 19, students will see that Pangaea formed during the Triassic period.)*

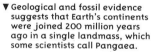

5 How Do Fossils Show the History of Earth's Species?

The fossil record provides the clues for your time line of Earth's history. Layers of rock can be rearranged by dramatic events such as volcanoes and earthquakes, but nowhere in the fossil record will you find anything out of order. There are no insect fossils from the Cambrian period. There are no flowering plant or bird fossils from the Devonian period. How can your time line help you find out even more about the fossils you examined in Lesson 2?

Exploration:
Find your fossil in time.

You need:
Fossils from Lesson 2
Classroom time line

❶ Take out the fossil that you examined before. Study the information that comes with the fossil.

❷ Examine the fossil again. What other living things existed when your fossil was alive?

❸ Locate your fossil on the time line. Draw a picture of it at the time it existed. ✎

Interpret your results.

- Which species on the time line appeared first?

- Which of the species you've studied is the most recent?

- Which species you've studied were on Earth 200 million years ago?

▼ Geological and fossil evidence suggests that Earth's continents were joined 200 million years ago in a single landmass, which some scientists call Pangaea.

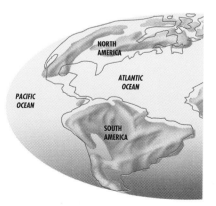

20 SUBCONCEPT ONE: FOSSILS AND EXTINCT SPECIES

Interpret Your Results

- Students will probably list living organisms at least as far back as the Cambrian period.
- Humans are the most recent of the living things.
- Turtles, reptiles, amphibians, insects, fish, and microscopic sea life were on Earth at that time.

Closer to Home: Cretaceous Park?

Have students review the topographical graph on page 19. Ask: **How did the earth's landforms change from the Jurassic to the Cretaceous periods?** *(There were more areas of water during the Jurassic period and the land was lush during the Cretaceous period.)*

Explain to students that a clone is an organism that is genetically identical to another organism.

- The remoteness of the habitat made it unlikely that many people would see a coelacanth until it was dead and probably unrecognizable.

- Answers should reflect the differences between cloning an extinct species and cloning an endangered species and suggest ways to save the endangered species instead of cloning them.

- Most filmmakers are more concerned with making an exciting and entertaining movie.

The ThinkMat for this lesson is a review of the first concept.

► The coelacanth has been called a "living fossil." This species has been on Earth for over 300 million years.

Closer to Home: Cretaceous Park?

Did you see the movie *Jurassic Park,* in which scientists cloned dinosaurs from DNA found in the blood of insects fossilized in amber? Then here's a surprise. Some of the movie's biggest and meanest movie stars—*Tyrannosaurus rex, Triceratops,* and *Velociraptor*—lived in the Cretaceous period, 70 million years after the Jurassic period.

Audiences usually forgive science bloopers like this because movies are entertaining. But you don't have to stretch the truth to find surprises in paleontology.

Imagine being a paleontologist in the 1930s. You were taught that coelacanths, a type of fossil fish, were extinct. You've examined million-year-old coelacanth fossils yourself. How do you feel when you open the newspaper one morning in 1938 and read that a live coelacanth had been caught off the coast of South Africa?

- Coelacanths today live in deep water off the coast of southern Africa. How do you think this habitat contributed to the belief that coelacanths were extinct?

- Do you think people should try cloning extinct animals, if it's possible? Why or why not? If your fellow scientists wanted to clone endangered animals to save them from extinction, how would you respond?

- Why do you think movies mix up science facts?

Think!

Why do you think scientists decided to divide geological time periods the way they do?

Think!

Scientists make such divisions so they can distinguish periods characterized by certain climates and forms of life.

LESSON THINKING SKILLS:
Organizing Information; Interpreting Graphs

21

Assessment Options

Using Students' Process Performance and Recorded Observations

Written Options

1. Students' responses on their LabMats and ThinkMat should give you a clear idea of their understanding of the lesson concept. Use Student Benchmarks to analyze their answers.

2. After the first Exploration, have students write captions for each period, using the information gathered on the time line.

Student Benchmarks

Proficient: Students discuss how Earth has undergone many changes in its history and how the history of many species is revealed in the fossil record.

Apprentice: Students discuss how fossils give clues to the earth's history. They can also place their fossils on the time line.

Novice: Students discuss how certain species have become extinct but may not know how fossils can give information about a species' history.

Portfolio

Students may decide they want to include the LabMats from this lesson as well as the captions from the Written Options in their Portfolio.

Oral Options

Listen to students as they do the Explorations. Student Benchmarks will give you an idea of how well they understand the lesson concept.

1. In Part One, lead students in a discussion of the different developments that took place during each period and between different periods. What were some major changes between the Cambrian and Jurassic periods?

2. In Part Two, ask students to identify the sources they use to place the fossils on the time line.

3. How students answer the Think question will also give you a good idea of their understanding of the lesson concept.

The following questions can also be used to assess understanding of the lesson concept:

4. What can fossils tell you about a species? *(Some possible answers may include a species' size or whether the species lived on land or in the ocean.)*

5. Name types of landforms where it's possible to see layers of rock that lie below the top layer of Earth and explain how these places might be beneficial to understanding Earth's history. *(Cliffs, outcroppings, canyons, riverbanks, caves, and craters may be mentioned. The visible layers may reveal fossils and other clues about Earth's prehistoric life and environments.)*

Reteaching the Novice

Have students walk along the class time line, identifying the geological periods and how long ago each existed. For each period, ask students what type of species existed. Had the environment changed? What about the climate? Ask students to compare the periods with one another and discuss the similarities and differences. Then ask

students to use the labels on the fossils to place their fossils on the class time line. You may wish to have students do research on their fossils beforehand.

Integrating Your Curriculum

INTEGRATING REFERENCE SOURCES

The Changing Earth

CHALLENGE · CHALLENGE

Have students find out what scientists think Earth's landmasses and oceans looked like at different geological times. Suggest that they look in reference books at the Jurassic period, the Cretaceous period, and the Paleocene epoch. During the Jurassic period there was one giant landmass called Pangaea. Dinosaurs roamed all over this continent and similar fossils from this period are found all over the world. In the Cretaceous period a sea called the Tethys split the land into chunks. During the Paleocene epoch the landmasses began dividing into the continents we know today.

Materials: markers, colored construction paper, scissors, glue

Make models of the landmasses during each period by cutting out shapes from colored paper.

• Paste them in the correct position or make jigsaw pieces of the continents so that they can be pushed together and moved around.

Students can display the models above the appropriate space on the class time line.

INTEGRATING ART

Dioramas

Have students make dioramas showing possible habitats and the organisms that lived in them during specific periods of Earth's history.

Materials for group of four: shoebox, paint, paper, oaktag, craft sticks, clay

Students can meet first to decide which period they want to choose, what environmental conditions they want to present, and which organisms they want to include.

• Tell students to divide responsibility for research and creation of the art project, with each student contributing to both.

INTEGRATING MATH: STATISTICS

Geologic Time

Homework Option

Have students use the figures on the time line on pages 18–19 to find the percentage of Earth's history represented by each period. Tell them to make a circle graph based on their calculations. With a circle graph students will see clearly that Earth's history is not divided into segments of equal lengths; some of the time periods are much longer than others.

CURIOSITY PLACE

Not all dinosaurs were giants. The smallest known dinosaur, *Compsognathus*, was about the size of a chicken.

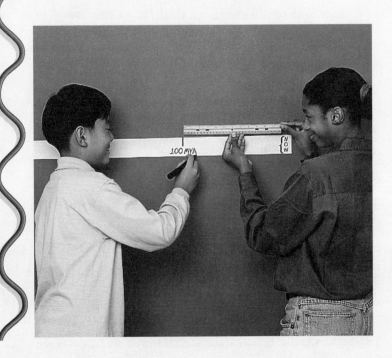

What Happened to the Dinosaurs?

Student Pages 22–25

Lesson Road Map

In the last lesson: Students discovered how fossils help to tell Earth's history.

In this lesson: Students evaluate several theories about the extinction of the dinosaur.

In the next lesson: Students will find out what affects the size of a population.

Getting Organized

This lesson requires one 40-minute session.

Materials per Group:
None

Advance Preparation:
none

The Story Line

Grade Level Concept
Different species have inhabited the earth at different times.

Subconcepts
Fossils provide evidence that many species that once inhabited the earth have become extinct.

Changes in the environment or human intervention can result in changes in the characteristics of a population, which are passed on to succeeding generations.

Variation and natural selection have resulted in the evolution of new species.

Lesson Concept
Dinosaurs may have become extinct as a result of changes in the environment.

ALSO FOR THIS LESSON:

ThinkMat 6

Thinking activity about the lesson

For Science Browsers

"Scientists Dig Up New Dinosaurs"
Student page 65

Content Background

What causes mass extinctions—the demise of many families of organisms—within a relatively short period of time? An unfavorable change in the environment is usually the cause. According to one estimate, two to four and a half families of organisms— each including many species—become extinct every million years.

The mass extinction that occurred 65 million years ago at the end of the Cretaceous period has puzzled scientists. Seventy percent of all known species of that period—including the dinosaurs—became extinct then. Several theories have been proposed to explain this phenomenon. Increased volcanic activity may have released dust and sulfur into the atmosphere, blocking out the sun and creating acid rain. The cooler climate and more acidic environment could have killed many life forms. Movements of the continents may also have contributed to climatic change. If a continent from a warm region drifted to a cooler region, certain plants and animals might not have survived. Evidence for the asteroid theory comes from the rock record. Around the world geologists have found in rocks a thin layer of iridium, a metal rare on Earth but commonly found in asteroids. Scientists think the iridium was fallout produced when a large asteroid crashed into Earth. The iridium layer lies between Mesozoic and Cenozoic sediments, indicating that the layer was formed at just the time of the Cretaceous extinction.

Vocabulary

extinction: The dying off of an entire species or population.

population: A group of organisms of the same species living in the same geographic area.

Teachers' Bookshelf

Bakker, Robert T. *The Dinosaurs Heresies.* New York: Zebra, 1988.

Raup, David M. *Extinction: Bad Genes or Bad Luck?* New York: W.W. Norton, 1991.

Theme Connection: Patterns of Change

Natural activities, such as volcanic eruptions and earthquakes, have caused changes in Earth's environments, which in turn have sometimes led to the extinction of species. Similarly, humans have developed and released into the environment toxic substances that have led to the endangerment of certain species.

Considering Second-Language Learners

Guide students in the reading of pages 22 and 23. Stop as necessary when students encounter difficult or unknown terms in the description of each theory regarding the extinction of dinosaurs. After the reading, group students into three teams. Each group will choose one of the theories described (asteroid, cosmic rays, or cooling) and make a poster to illustrate it. Help them label their posters. Have each team make a class presentation with their finished poster. Ask students to explain what their poster represents, using the vocabulary they've learned thus far. In an open discussion, encourage the rest of the class to determine how much of what they see in the poster was described in the lesson and how much was invented or imagined by the students who made the poster.

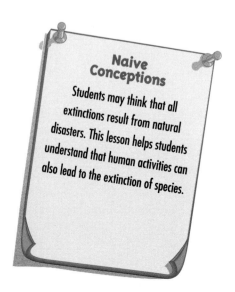

Naive Conceptions

Students may think that all extinctions result from natural disasters. This lesson helps students understand that human activities can also lead to the extinction of species.

LESSON 6

SCIENCE LITERACY:
Recognize cause and effect.

Thinking Skills and Objectives

Students will:

- **interpret graphs** to find out how global temperature and precipitation have changed over time

- **formulate hypotheses** about how dinosaurs became extinct

Opening the Discussion

Let students refer to the time line on pages 18–19 in Lesson 5 and have them describe the climate, environment, plants, and animals during the Jurassic period.

Before students read page 22, have them study the illustration on pages 22–23. Ask: **What are some characteristics that the animals share?** (*Most are large and seem to have tough skins. They also have either sharp teeth, horns, or claws.*) **Since the artist wasn't alive at the time when dinosaurs existed how did the artist get the information for the illustration?** (*Probably through research that scientists have compiled from the fossil record.*) Write students' ideas on the Recording Board.

Diverse perspectives

Today only two species survive from a group of animals called *proboscidea*, long-nosed beasts that once numbered over 300 species. The survivors are the elephants of Africa and Asia. The great size of these creatures protects them from all predators except humans. Humans pose a threat to elephants by turning their habitats into farms and by hunting them. As a result African and Asian countries have reserved land in national parks for the elephants.

LESSON 6

What Happened to the Dinosaurs?

Imagine the last *Tyrannosaurus rex* waking up one morning about 65 million years ago. It's starving. One day, a year before, the earth beneath its feet shook and it couldn't see the sun; for weeks afterward, the sky was darkened by black dust and clouds of ash. All the plants died, and plant-eating dinosaurs began to die, too. For a while, the T-rex and its fellow meat-eaters had plenty to eat. Finally their food supply ran out and the meat-eaters had to kill and eat each other. The last T-rex is so weak from hunger it doesn't even stir as a prehistoric bird flies overhead. When the sun rises again, *Tyrannosaurus rex* will be extinct.

Fossil evidence suggests that dinosaurs had ruled the earth for 150 million years when they died out 65 million years ago. There are many explanations for the extinction, or dying off, of the dinosaurs. One theory is that one or more asteroids crashed into the planet. An asteroid is a chunk of metal or rock that orbits the sun. The impact of the crash surrounded Earth with a dark cloud that made photosynthesis impossible for months. Plants died, the larger plant-eating animals starved, and then the larger meat-eating animals starved. No more dinosaurs.

But not everyone agrees with the asteroid theory. Some scientists blame dinosaur extinction on cosmic rays released by star clusters exploding millions of miles out in space; others, on changes in Earth's climate caused by volcanic eruptions.

Other scientists think the shifting of Earth's large landmasses may have caused the extinctions. Some say this shifting caused the cooling of the planet and the drying up of the inland seas. Another large group of scientists thinks the shifting caused land bridges to form between former islands. This could have killed off the dinosaurs by exposing them to predators and diseases they didn't have before.

There are many theories to explain the extinction of the dinosaurs. Which of the explanations you've just read seems the most likely to you?

22 SUBCONCEPT ONE: FOSSILS AND EXTINCT SPECIES

Student Pages 22–23

SCIENCE LITERACY:
Recognize cause and effect.

After students have read the text, ask: **What might have happened to the dinosaurs if their environment had changed differently? For instance, what if the climate had gotten colder or drier? if new predators had appeared?** *(Accept any reasonable answer that shows students have applied what they learned about environmental changes.)*

Have students identify the different theories for the mass extinction of dinosaurs. List each theory on the chalkboard. **Which of the theories do you think makes the most sense? Why?** *(Accept any answer that indicates students have logically expanded on the information given and what they've learned in previous lessons.)*

What kind of evidence would you need to determine whether or not the theory was right? *(You would need physical evidence, such as markings at the site where the asteroid landed, fossils showing specific environmental changes, radioactive dating or ice-core samples, and so on.)*

Fossil evidence shows that dinosaurs like *Tyrannosaurus rex*, *Triceratops*, and others became extinct at about the same time. What change in their environment could have caused this?

Information Connection:
Interpreting graphs

Draw students' attention to the line variations in the temperature section of the graph. Ask: **What is the difference between the sharp jagged portions of the line and the curved sections?** *(The jagged sections represent abrupt fluctuations, or extremes in temperature, in short periods of time while the curved sections represent more gradual changes over longer periods of time.)*

From the graph, students will see that during the Triassic, Jurassic, and Cretaceous periods the temperatures were warm and there was little rain or snow.

After the Precambrian era the next two periods during which ice ages took place were the Ordovician period and the Carboniferous period. Both these periods were cold and wet.

If dinosaurs existed today, they'd probably feel most at home in a warm, wet climate, such as a rain forest. They would be comfortable in climates that most resemble the Triassic, Jurassic, and Cretaceous periods. (Even though these periods had little rainfall, the air was very moist with humidity.)

We live in the Quaternary period, and the temperature, rainfall, and snowfall tend to be moderate. During the end of the Carboniferous period the climate was wet and cold.

This is a good time to distribute ThinkMat 6.

Diverse perspectives

All five species of rhinoceros, which inhabit Asia and Africa, are currently threatened with extinction. The reason lies in the rhino's most distinctive feature—its large horn or horns. Although many countries have made it illegal to hunt rhinoceroses, they're still being wiped out by poachers. In the African nations of Kenya and Zimbabwe special teams of rangers are assigned to protect these animals.

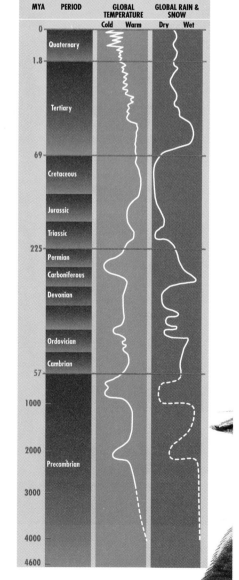

6 What Happened to the Dinosaurs?

Information Connection:
Interpreting graphs

Changes in Earth's climate may—or may not—have been responsible for the extinction of dinosaur populations. A population is a group of organisms of the same species living in the same area. But whatever the effect of the climate on dinosaur populations, there's no doubt that climate helped dinosaurs to thrive during the Triassic, Jurassic, and Cretaceous periods. Read the graph. Were these periods cold or warm? Were they dry or wet?

Some scientists believe that a change in climate at the end of the Cretaceous period caused winters to become too cold for the dinosaurs. Unlike mammals or birds, dinosaurs had no fur or feathers.

Radioactive dating, ice core sampling and chemical analysis of fossils provide information on the history of Earth's climate. According to this data, there have been several periods in which sheets of ice covered large regions of the planet. Each of these ice ages lasted several million years.

Look at the graph again. An ice age took place about 600 million years ago, at the end of the Precambrian period. During which two periods did the next ice ages take place? What do these periods have in common? In what parts of the world today do you think a dinosaur would feel at home? Why?

How does the climate of your own geological time period compare to the climate at the end of the Carboniferous period? Which climate do you think you would prefer?

▶ Compared to other periods in Earth's history, has there been more or less rain and snow during our own period?

MYA	PERIOD	GLOBAL TEMPERATURE		GLOBAL RAIN & SNOW	
		Cold	Warm	Dry	Wet
0	Quaternary				
1.8					
	Tertiary				
69	Cretaceous				
	Jurassic				
	Triassic				
225	Permian				
	Carboniferous				
	Devonian				
	Ordovician				
	Cambrian				
57					
1000					
2000	Precambrian				
3000					
4000					
4600					

24 SUBCONCEPT ONE: FOSSILS AND EXTINCT SPECIES

Closer to Home: *Extinct* means gone forever.

Have students review the photographs and captions. Ask students: **Can you think of ways to save the black lace cactus and the California condor?** *(Forbid collecting of the cactus and start captive breeding programs for both.)*

Explain to students that extinction is a natural phenomenon, no matter who or what is responsible. We're all a part of nature. According to the fossil record 999 out of every 1,000 species that ever lived are now extinct.

• The extinction of other species could threaten the survival of human beings if people relied on the species for food, for protection from other species (as we rely on bats to keep down the insect population), for oxygen (as we rely on trees and plants), and so on.

This would be a good opportunity to have students get on-line to share ideas about endangered species.

▲ Black lace cactus is now so rare that it's only found in Texas.

▲ You aren't likely to see a California condor outside a zoo.

Closer to Home:
***Extinct* means gone forever.**

The disappearance of species didn't begin or end with the extinction of dinosaurs. Scientists figure that 999 out of every 1,000 species that ever lived are now extinct. So why are some people making such a big fuss about the number of species dying out all over the planet?

What's frightening about extinctions today is that humans are speeding them up. Humans overhunt for food and kill animals for sport. We trap animals for their furs and kill them for their tusks and horns. We allow domestic animals to crowd out wildlife. As the human population grows, we crowd out many wild plants and animals by destroying their habitats.

• How do you think the extinction of other species might threaten the survival of human beings?

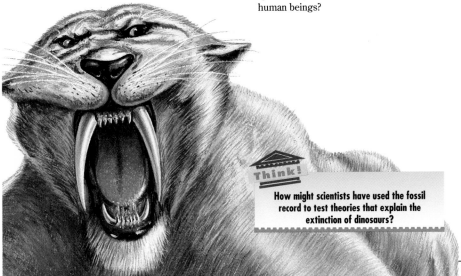

▼ Saber-toothed tigers became extinct 10,000 years ago.

Think!

How might scientists have used the fossil record to test theories that explain the extinction of dinosaurs?

Think!

From the fossil record, scientists might be able to find out how the climate changed and what other living organisms survived or became extinct.

LESSON THINKING SKILLS:
Interpreting Graphs; Recognizing Cause and Effect

25

Assessment Options

Using Students' Process Performance and Recorded Observations

Written Options

1. Students' responses on their ThinkMat should give you a clear idea of their understanding of the lesson concept. Use Student Benchmarks to analyze their answers.

2. In addition, after discussing how dinosaurs may have become extinct, have students write a paragraph about the changes in the environment that affect their lives.

Student Benchmarks

Proficient: Students evaluate and propose theories to explain the dinosaur's extinction. They'll also propose ways to save endangered species.

Apprentice: Students discuss several theories about the extinction of the dinosaurs and connect them to changes in the environment.

Novice: Students discuss that dinosaurs became extinct, but may not understand how environmental changes caused their extinction.

Portfolio

Students may decide they want to include the ThinkMat from this lesson in their Portfolio. In addition, they may want to add one of the Options.

Oral Options

Here are some ideas for class discussion of this content lesson. Student Benchmarks will give you an idea of how well students understand the lesson concept.

1. After reviewing all the theories for the extinction of dinosaurs, have students think of ways to prevent the extinction of some of today's endangered species. What type of environmental changes have affected the endangered species of today?

2. How students answer the Think question will also give you a good idea of their understanding of the lesson concept.

The following questions can also be used to assess understanding of the lesson concept:

3. How do you think history might be different if dinosaurs hadn't become extinct? *(Students may have many ideas, such as: if the reign of the dinosaurs had continued to the present, humans wouldn't have existed because mammals wouldn't have dominated.)*

4. What are some reasons people may give for and against attempting to prevent extinction of a species? *(Reasons for preventing extinction may include maintaining ecological diversity and allowing all species a right to exist. Reasons against might include that it's part of the natural process for species to come and go or that we don't have enough resources or influence to address all the threats to every endangered species.)*

Reteaching the Novice

Review each theory with students. Have students select a theory they think is the most logical. Ask them to go to the library to find out more about the theory they chose. Why do you think your theory is more believable than the others? Have students share any new information with the class.

Integrating Your Curriculum

INTEGRATING SOCIAL STUDIES: CAUSE AND EFFECT

The Return of the Falcon

CHALLENGE · CHALLENGE ·

Students may also be interested in learning about endangered species success stories, such as that of the peregrine falcon, which was rescued from the brink of extinction and may soon be taken off the endangered species list. Have students research the peregrine falcon or another species and make a storyboard. For each frame they can show a step of its history: which human habits threatened its environment, how its numbers dwindled, discoveries that were made about its adaptability to urban environments, and how committed people helped bring the falcons back. Have students write text to accompany their illustrations. Encourage them to use comic-strip dialogue balloons, too.

FIELD TRIP

Going, Going, Gone

If possible, arrange to take students to a natural history museum, where they can see fossils as well as models of dinosaurs. Have students prepare for the trip by brainstorming what they already know about paleontology and making a list of questions about dinosaurs they'd like to find answers to. After the trip, give students a chance to review some of their early ideas about dinosaurs. Have students work in groups, with each group contributing a page to a book that includes illustrations and a question and detailed answer about dinosaurs. If computer equipment is available, students may want to desktop-publish their book and/or create computer graphics for it. Let them brainstorm titles and vote on which to use (for example, *Everything You Always Wanted to Know About Dinosaurs* or *The Ten Most Common Questions Asked About Dinosaurs*).

USING THE LIBRARY

Express Yourself

Homework Option

Have students go to the library to find out about plants and animals that are in danger of becoming extinct in their region. Tell them to choose one endangered species, find out more about why it is endangered, and write a letter explaining how the species could be saved. Help students decide where they can send their letters (senators, congresspeople, and so on) in order to have the greatest impact. For further information on endangered species in the United States, students can write to U.S. National Fish and Wildlife Service, Publications Unit, 4401 North Fairfax Dr., Mailstop 103WEBB, Arlington, VA 22203.

CURIOSITY PLACE

The greatest extinction of them all occurred at the end of the Permian period, when 96 percent of all species died out.

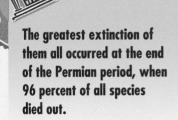

What Affects the Size of a Population?

Student Pages 26–29

Lesson Road Map

In the last lesson: Students evaluated several theories about the extinction of the dinosaur.

In this lesson: Students find out what affects the size of a population. In Part One they observe how a population can grow in the absence of predators. In Part Two they observe the effects of prey and predator populations on each other.

In the next lesson: Students will observe how members of a population differ and compete.

The Story Line

Grade Level Concept
Different species have inhabited the earth at different times.

Subconcepts
Fossils provide evidence that many species that once inhabited the earth have become extinct.

Changes in the environment or human intervention can result in changes in the characteristics of a population, which are passed on to succeeding generations.

Variation and natural selection have resulted in the evolution of new species.

Lesson Concept
With abundant food and no predators a population grows, but populations that interact affect each other.

Getting Organized

This lesson requires one 40-minute session and one 45-minute session.

Materials per Group:
3 sheets of paper
Coins
Scissors

PART ONE

Advance Preparation:
Gather materials.

Materials per Group:
Scissors
ThinkMat 7
Number cube

PART TWO

Advance Preparation:
Gather materials.

ALSO FOR THIS LESSON:

ThinkMat 7	LabMats 7A and 7B	For Science Browsers
For use with the Exploration	Recording sheets for the Explorations	"Sharks" Student page 64

Content Background

A nimal and plant populations tend to be relatively stable in size, except for species newly introduced to an area or those headed for extinction. In other words, death rates roughly equal birth rates. So what factors affect population size?

Theoretically, in an environment with no factors to limit growth—an environment with unlimited resources, no predators, and no diseases—births would exceed deaths and a population would grow rapidly. In the real world, however, many factors limit population growth, including limited resources, loss of habitat, intraspecies competition, diseases, and predation.

The interplay between a prey population and its predators is complicated. Generally, if there's an increase or decrease in the prey population, a corresponding increase or decrease in the predator population usually follows.

You could say that the interaction between the two species leads to a balance in the populations. When a prey population loses its predators entirely, however, the balance is upset. Let's say that wolves, the natural predators of deer, are driven from an area. As a result the deer population may increase dramatically, exhaust its food supplies, and damage its environment to such a degree that starvation and a rapid decline in the deer population would result.

For much of human history, its population growth rate has remained relatively stable. Since the Industrial Revolution, however, death rates have dropped (especially infant mortality rates) and the population has grown rapidly. Improved technology for food production, improved medical care, and increased knowledge of nutrition and sanitation have all played a role in this dramatic rise in population.

Theme Connection: Patterns of Change

T he interaction between predator and prey populations affects how the size of each group changes over time. Similarly, the rate of human population growth has been affected by technological advances in the fields of medicine, communications, and nutrition.

Considering Second-Language Learners

G et illustrated books from the library about animal life in various regions of the world. Encourage students to share any stories or information they might know about the animals described in the books. To help them develop their oral skills in English while encouraging hypothetical thinking, propose a game of "What If?" For example, if you're focusing on pandas with your students, ask them to come up with answers to the question: "What if we bring pandas to live here?" Lead students to imagine what life would be like for the pandas. Help them identify details about the pandas' natural habitat in China and compare them with conditions in their hometown. Prompt students with simple questions such as: "Will they be cold or hot? Will they have their favorite food?"

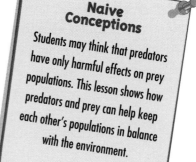

Naive Conceptions

Students may think that predators have only harmful effects on prey populations. This lesson shows how predators and prey can help keep each other's populations in balance with the environment.

What do we know?
What do we want to know?

1 ACTIVATE

EXPLORATION:
Make a population model.

Process Skills and Objectives

Students will:

- **predict** the effects of a rabbit population with adequate food supplies, no predators, and a continuation of the breeding pattern

- **compare** the patterns of growth and decline in the rabbit population

Opening the Discussion

Ask students to read the introductory paragraph on page 26. Have them think about the previous lesson in which they learned about the extinction of the dinosaur. Review some of the natural, environmental changes that might have caused the dinosaurs' extinction.

Ask: **What are some human activities that can lead to the extinction of a species?** *(overhunting animals for food or furs/skins; capturing rare animals to sell as pets; allowing domestic animals to crowd out wildlife; or destroying habitats through development or environmental pollution)* Write their answers on the Recording Board.

PREPARING FOR THE EXPLORATION

Materials per Group: 3 sheets of paper, coins, scissors

Suggested Grouping: pairs

Approximate Time: 25 minutes

Classroom Management: Copy LabMat 7A. You could jigsaw this lesson by assigning the Explorations on pages 26 and 28 to different groups to do at the same time. After they've shared results, complete the Exploration Connection and Closer to Home.

LESSON 7

What Affects the Size of a Population?

The extinction of one population sometimes gives an opportunity to another population. That's why the Age of Age of Mammals began when the Age of Dinosaurs ended. By studying fossils and life on the planet today, you can learn about the kinds of things that affect the size of a population and its survival.

Exploration:
Make a population model.

You need:
Paper
Coins
Scissors

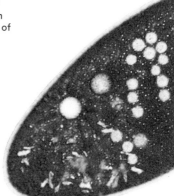

▲ A paramecium under a microscope

❶ Draw 12 penny–sized circles on a sheet of paper, and cut them out. Each of these tokens represents one rabbit. Turn another sheet of paper 90 degrees. Draw five circles across the top. Each circle represents one breeding period. On Rabbit Island, a pair of rabbits produces another pair each breeding period. The rabbits live for three breeding periods.

❷ Place the rabbit tokens on circle 1. Write "1" on these tokens and on the tokens representing the first pair produced. Record the total number of rabbits.

❸ Move the rabbits to circle 2. Here each pair produces two new offspring. Write "2" on the new tokens and record the total number of rabbits. ✏

❹ Keep moving the rabbits ahead until they reach circle 5. On each new circle, have each pair of rabbits produce two offspring. Record the total number of rabbits, and then remove the rabbits who were born three circles earlier. If you need more rabbits, make some tokens! ✏

Interpret your results.

- How long did it take the rabbit population to reach 16?

- What pattern of growth do you see in the rabbit population?

- What would happen if rabbits reproduced in this pattern without any natural or human control?

26 SUBCONCEPT TWO: HOW MEMBERS OF SPECIES CHANGE

EXPLORATION:
Make a population model.

❶❷ Ask: What effect does removing pairs of rabbits after three breeding periods have on the population growth? *(a slight decrease)* Distribute LabMat 7A.

🌀 Troubleshooting: Be sure students remove rabbit pairs that have gone through three breeding periods but only *after* the rabbits have bred and the total number of rabbits for that breeding period has been counted.

❸❹ What would happen if the rabbits had more offspring each breeding period? if they could breed for five breeding cycles rather than three? *(In each case the population would grow faster.)*

Interpret Your Results

- The rabbit population reached 16 on the third circle. There were 48 rabbits on the fifth circle.
- The rabbit population grows faster and faster.
- The rabbit population would get so large that there wouldn't be enough food to sustain it.

Exploration Connection:
Interpreting graphs

SIZES OF PARAMECIUM POPULATIONS

From the graph, students will see that when the two species of paramecium were grown separately, the population of species A grew more rapidly. When the two species were grown together, the growth of both populations was inhibited. Species B was affected most in a negative way because its population was more inhibited. Students may suggest that species A prevented species B from getting food; that species A ate most of the food before species B had a chance to; or that species A reproduces more rapidly than species B does.

Have students read the caption about the wild rabbits in Australia. Since the rabbits that were brought to Australia had few natural predators, their population grew unchecked so that their main source of food, the grass, began to be depleted after a period of time.

Exploration Connection:
Interpreting graphs

Paramecia are microscopic, single-celled organisms that live in many ponds and streams. Like rabbits, paramecia grow quickly if they have plenty to eat and if there are no natural enemies around. But the size reached by a paramecium population can be greatly affected if another paramecium population comes along and competes with it.

Look at the graph above. It shows the sizes reached by two paramecium populations in an experiment. The two paramecia show population sizes reached when

the two populations were grown separately, using separate food sources. The bars show population sizes reached when the populations were grown together, using the same food source.

When the two populations were grown separately, which population grew larger? What happened when the two populations were grown together? Which population was most affected by being grown with the other species? What reasons can you think of for this difference?

WILD RABBITS IN AUSTRALIA

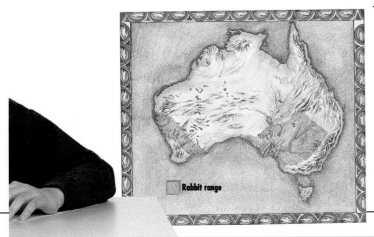

◄ English settlers brought European rabbits to Australia in order to hunt and eat them. The settlers didn't think about bringing along the natural predators that control the rabbit population in England. How does this explain the fact that, within a hundred years, rabbits had eaten the country's grass down to the ground?

Rabbit range

27

2

EXPLORE

EXPLORATION:
Play Rabbit and Fox.

Process Skills and Objectives

Students will:

- **communicate** that a population will grow rapidly in somewhat predictable patterns if there are no predators and plenty of food, but less predictably if there's competition for food

- **compare** the differences between the breeding rabbits and the nonbreeding fox in terms of population growth

PREPARING FOR THE EXPLORATION

Materials per Group: scissors, ThinkMat 7, number cube

Suggested Grouping: pairs

Approximate Time: 30 minutes

Classroom Management: Copy LabMat 7B and ThinkMat 7. Have students take turns moving the rabbit tokens and recording the results.

EXPLORATION:
Play Rabbit and Fox.

❶ ❷ Tell students that when a rabbit lands on the same spot as the fox, it doesn't get eaten by the fox. Distribute LabMat 7B.

⊚ **Troubleshooting:** Since this game is somewhat complicated, you might have a pair of volunteers demonstrate the game before the entire class plays.

❸ ❹ Ask: **What would happen if the rabbits quadrupled when they landed on the breed square?** *(It would take longer for the fox to starve.)*

❺ Have students predict how the relative speeds of the fox and rabbits will affect the outcome. **What would happen to the two populations if the fox was breeding, too?** *(More foxes would mean that the rabbit population would decline faster. If it declined too far, some foxes would starve, and the fox population would decline.)*

---

7 What Affects the Size of a Population?

In nature, few animals are without natural enemies. What do you think would happen to the rabbit population on Rabbit Island if a few foxes swam over from the mainland one day, and liked the menu so much they decided to stay?

Exploration:
Play Rabbit and Fox.

You need:
Scissors
ThinkMat 7B
Number cube

❶ Cut out the animal tokens. Place one fox on the F square and three rabbits on the R square. Roll the number cube to find out how many squares the fox moves. Subtract that number from 6 to find out how many squares the rabbits move. (Example: If you roll a 2, the fox moves 2 and the rabbits move 4.) If you roll a 6, both rabbits and fox move 6 squares per turn. Record the data. ✎

❷ The fox moves first. Each time it catches up with the rabbits, it stops to eat. You take one rabbit off.

❸ Then the rabbits move, doubling each time they reach a Breed square. Add tokens to the square.

❹ Rabbits and fox take turns moving until the rabbits reach the end or are eaten. The fox starves if it hasn't caught a rabbit when it reaches the end.

❺ Play six times, and record the results of each game. If you roll a number you've already used, roll again for a new number. ✎

Interpret your results.

- What speeds (number of squares per turn) for fox and rabbits resulted in the rabbits being killed off right away? What speeds resulted in the fox starving?

- What speeds resulted in both fox and rabbits surviving a long time?

- In the wild, what would happen if rabbits were much slower than foxes? much faster than foxes?

- How would you explain the fact that in nature foxes and rabbits live and thrive in the same area?

▲ Humans have few natural predators. What limits the size of human populations?

28   SUBCONCEPT TWO: HOW MEMBERS OF SPECIES CHANGE

Interpret Your Results

- a fox speed of 5 and a rabbit's speed of 1; any time the rabbits were faster than or as fast as the fox
- when the fox had a speed of 4 and the rabbits had a speed of 2
- The foxes would eat all the rabbits. Faster rabbits would multiply until there were so many of them that there wouldn't be enough food and they'd starve, too.
- Both are able to maintain stable population sizes.

Closer to Home: How many people are there?

After students have studied the population graph, ask them: **Could you use a graph to show human population growth for more than 25,000 years?** *(Graphs can show any number relationship. You would just use larger numbers for the years shown on the axis.)*

- The population was less than 10 million. Students may suggest that there were more natural predators.

- Answers will vary, but students should realize that there will be an increase; some reasons may include better nutrition and health care.

- Answers will vary, but students will probably recall that an increase in human population may mean the destruction of some plant and animal habitats.

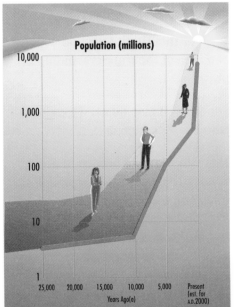

WORLD POPULATION OVER TIME

Closer to Home: How many people are there?

Do you know the population of the town or city where you live? Do you think it has changed over the last ten years? Human populations are constantly changing around the world. The graph to the left shows an estimate of how the world population as a whole has changed over the past 25,000 years.

- What general statement can you make about the world population before 10,000 years ago? What factors do you think might have caused this to be true?
- Based on this graph, what would you predict the world population will be in 2050? Explain.
- How do changes in human populations affect other populations? How do changes in human populations affect you?

Think!

Suppose a severe dry spell killed most of the plants on Rabbit Island. How would this affect the rabbit population there? How would it affect the fox population?

Think!

Ask students to make a list of how a drought would affect both populations. A severe drought might kill all the animals. More likely, enough rabbits will die to both reduce the fox population and allow the vegetation to recover.

LESSON THINKING SKILLS:
Recognizing Patterns and Relationships; Interpreting Graphs

29

Assessment Options

Using Students' Process Performance and Recorded Observations

Written Options

1. Students' responses on their LabMats and ThinkMat should give you a clear idea of their understanding of the lesson concept. Use Student Benchmarks to analyze their answers.

2. In addition, have students compare the two Explorations and make lists, identifying the similarities and differences in both games.

Student Benchmarks

Proficient: Students discuss how food supply and predators affect the size of a population and how one population affects the growth of another through competition or predation.

Apprentice: Students discuss that a population will grow with plenty of food and no predators, and that populations have an effect on one another in the way they interact.

Novice: Students realize that food supply and predators are related to the size of a population, but may not understand the way populations interact.

Portfolio

Students may decide they want to include the LabMats from this lesson in their Portfolio. In addition, they may want to add one of the Options on page 59.

Oral Options

Listen to students as they do the Explorations. Student Benchmarks will give you an idea of how well they understand the lesson concept.

1. In Part One, ask students questions about real-life situations that might affect the breeding pattern of the rabbits, such as harsh weather or obstacles due to land formations (rambles and swamps).

2. In Part Two, lead students into a discussion of how other living things, such as birds, plants, or squirrels, might interact with the rabbits and fox.

3. How students answer the Think question will also give you a good idea of their understanding of the lesson concept.

The following questions can also be used to assess understanding of the lesson concept:

4. Why is it necessary to regulate human hunting of animal populations? *(Too many human predators can cause the decline of an animal population, affecting the balance of other populations that interact with that animal population.)*

5. How might human settlements in an animal population's habitat affect the population growth of that species? *(Human settlement would take up living space and disrupt the food supplies within the habitat, causing a decline in the animal population's growth rate.)*

Reteaching the Novice

Have students add two natural disturbances to each game, such as a landslide, volcanic eruption, earthquake, tornado, or hurricane. If an animal lands on that space, remove the token from the game board. After students have replayed the games, tell them to compare the games with the original ones. Ask them to make a list of how the results differed. Lead a discussion on how natural disturbances can disrupt the habitats for animal, plant, and human populations.

Integrating Your Curriculum

INTEGRATING MATH: STATISTICS

Human Population

CHALLENGE · CHALLENGE

Have students find population figures for your town, city, or state for the twentieth century. Have them plot the information on a graph. Then have them make predictions about future growth or decline in population and plot another graph for the twenty-first century. Have them write down factors they think have affected the population thus far in the twentieth century and factors they think will affect the population in the twenty-first century. These might include war, natural disasters, improvements in medicine and nutrition, a change from rural to urban living, and so on.

INTEGRATING REFERENCE SOURCES

Marsupials

Marsupials flourished in South America until the continent drifted into North America. Other types of mammals then outcompeted the marsupials, so only a few forms of marsupials are left in North and South America today. The most common is the opossum. In Australia, however, marsupials evolved in isolation. They didn't have to compete with other mammals and were able to fill many environmental niches. Have kids find out about interesting marsupials and what environmental niches they fill, and then draw a family tree of related marsupials. Ask them to label each animal and make the lines of descent clear.

INTEGRATING SOCIAL STUDIES: CAUSE AND EFFECT

World Population Size

Homework Option

Explain to students that the population of the world increases by about two people every second. That means that every year during the 1990s the world adds as many people as currently live in Central America. Ask students to find out how this rapid growth is affecting such things as food supply and energy use. What recommendations are being made to remedy the rapid population growth? They might discover, for example, that education seems to have the most direct effect on lessening the rate of population growth. Have students write short essays, using their research as a guide, to come up with solutions to controlling population growth.

CURIOSITY PLACE

In just seven months one pair of cockroaches could have 164 million descendants.

How Do Members of a Population Differ and Compete?

Student Pages 30–33

Lesson Road Map

In the last lesson: Students found out what affects the size of a population.

In this lesson: Students observe how members of a population differ and compete.

In the next lesson: Students will demonstrate in a game how traits are passed from parents to offspring.

The Story Line

Grade Level Concept
Different species have inhabited the earth at different times.

Subconcepts
Fossils provide evidence that many species that once inhabited the earth have become extinct.

Changes in the environment or human intervention can result in changes in the characteristics of a population, which are passed on to succeeding generations.

Variation and natural selection have resulted in the evolution of new species.

Lesson Concept
Traits differ among members of a population, with certain traits providing competitive advantages.

Getting Organized

This lesson requires one 50-minute session.

Materials per Group:
40 unshelled peanuts
Ruler
ThinkMat 8

Advance Preparation:
Gather materials.

ALSO FOR THIS LESSON:

ThinkMat 8

For use with the Exploration

LabMat 8

Recording sheet for the Exploration

Content Background

Individuals in a population or species are similar, but they aren't identical. There's quite a bit of genetic variation within a species. Individuals can inherit different traits through mutation or through the recombination of genes that occurs in sexual reproduction. Some of these traits may give certain individuals a better chance of survival than others. These individuals may live longer and produce more offspring, who in turn inherit these favorable traits.

Generally you can graph the variation of a trait within a population as a bell-shaped curve. That is, most members of a population display a "medium" form of a trait, while a few individuals display "extreme" forms. For instance, the birth weights of most newborns fall into a middle range, while a few babies have either extremely low or extremely high birth weights. Researchers have found that babies with birth weights in the middle range are more likely to survive and thus reproduce offspring of a similar birth weight.

There's usually intense competition between members of a population when resources such as food or territory are scarce. Animals that compete successfully for food will be healthier and better able to survive and reproduce. Cooperation can also be a major factor for survival. In some species, parents may work together to care for their young, ensuring healthier young than an individual parent could raise alone. Some animals, such as lions and wolves, hunt in groups to increase their chances of successful competition.

Vocabulary

variations: Differences between members of the same species.

Teachers' Bookshelf

Stein, Sara. *The Evolution Book.* New York: Workman, 1986.

Wilson, Edward O. *The Diversity of Life.* New York: W. W. Norton, 1992.

Theme Connection: Patterns of Change

Change seems to be the one constant in life. Genetics influences the variations in traits among members of a population. Similarly, the environment influences how living species evolve.

Considering Second-Language Learners

Write the verb *compete* on the chalkboard. Ask students to think of words that are related to *compete* (*competition* and *competitive*). Clarify the meaning of *compete* for them, if necessary, using the students' preferred bilingual dictionary. It's important for students to understand that words take different forms depending on their use. Write the verb *differ* on the chalkboard. Lead students to understand its connection to the word *different* and *difference*.

Naive Conceptions

Students may think that competition only takes place in sports and contests. This lesson shows how living things—including humans—compete in many different ways, and how certain inherited traits can give some individuals a competitive advantage over others.

What do we know?
What do we want to know?

1

ACTIVATE

LESSON 8

EXPLORATION:
Sort and measure peanuts.

Process Skills and Objectives

Students will:

● **observe** variations in a population of peanuts

● **communicate** that competition doesn't necessarily involve aggression

● **measure** the various lengths of peanuts

Opening the Discussion

Lead students in a discussion on how members of a family can differ in appearance even though they may have the same biological parents.

Ask: **Have you ever noticed how your friend looks different from her or his mother, father, sister, or brother? How do they differ?** *(Answers will vary but students will probably mention size, coloring, hair texture, and facial features.)*

Have students read the first paragraph on page 30. Write students' answers to the question in the text on the Recording Board.

Student Pages 30–31

PREPARING FOR THE EXPLORATION

Materials per Group: 40 unshelled peanuts; ruler; ThinkMat 8

Suggested Grouping: four

Approximate Time: 20 minutes

Classroom Management: Copy LabMat 8 and ThinkMat 8. Students who finish first can do one of the Options on page 67.

LESSON 8

How Do Members of a Population Differ and Compete?

What else do populations do besides grow or disappear? Just take a look at any population: a bed of tulips, for example, or a flock of pigeons in the park. Look closely. They're not all the same. How do you think the individuals in one population differ from each other?

Exploration:
Sort and measure peanuts.

You need:
40 unshelled peanuts
Ruler
ThinkMat 8

❶ Open the bag of peanuts. Take the peanuts from the bag one at a time.

❷ Measure each peanut with your ruler. Find the column on your ThinkMat that describes the length of the peanut and fill in one square. Keep track of the longest and shortest peanuts.

❸ When you've finished measuring the peanuts, one square on the ThinkMat should be filled in for every peanut you measured. Count the peanuts and the filled-in squares to make sure you've measured each of the 40 peanuts.

Interpret your results.

● How long were your longest and shortest peanuts? If there were more than one of either length, how many were there?

● Which column had the largest number of peanuts? How many peanuts were in that column?

● How many peanuts were longer than the peanuts in the longest column? How many were shorter?

● Based on your observations, what can you say about how peanuts vary in length?

▶ Because it finds most of its food up high, a giraffe with a slightly longer neck has an advantage when it competes for food. When do you think a longer neck could become a disadvantage to a giraffe?

30 SUBCONCEPT TWO: HOW MEMBERS OF SPECIES CHANGE

EXPLORATION:
Sort and measure peanuts.

❶ Tell students that they'll be making a graph that shows the pattern of variation in the lengths of peanut shells. Distribute LabMat 8.

🌀 **Troubleshooting:** Be sure students make random selections of peanuts. Suggest that they close their eyes as they reach in the bag.

❷ Demonstrate how to measure a peanut accurately so that all students measure the same way.

❸ Ask: **Why are graphs useful for organizing this kind of information?** (*Graphs can help us see patterns in data and make predictions based on those patterns.*)

Interpret Your Results

- The longest peanuts will usually be less than 6 cm (2 in.) long. The shortest peanuts will usually be about 1 cm (1/3 in.) long.
- the column with the medium-length peanuts
- Answers will vary.
- There's great variation but most peanuts are of medium length.

WEIGHT OF HUMANS AT BIRTH

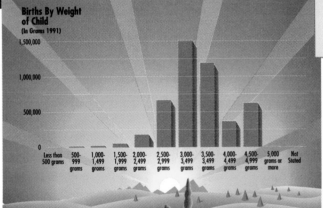

Births By Weight of Child
(In Grams 1991)

Exploration Connection:
Interpreting graphs

If you examine the graph on your ThinkMat again, you'll see that the lengths of the peanuts make a pattern. There may be small differences, but most of your peanut shells are probably middle length, with a few that are shorter and a few that are longer. Differences—such as height and weight—in members of the same species are called variations.

Look at the graph at the top of the page. Compare it to the graph you filled out in the Exploration. How are they both different from the graph on page 29?

Two of these graphs show a pattern of variation that takes its name from the shape of the data when you connect the tops of the bars—a bell curve. Draw a line connecting the tops of the columns on your ThinkMat. What pattern do you see?

If you used a bell curve to describe giraffe necks, the longest necks would be at one end of the curve. Which necks would be at the other end?

Look at the graph again. Based on the data given, how many grams would you expect a newborn baby to weigh?

Exploration Connection:
Interpreting graphs

Students will see that the graph on this page and the graph in the Exploration both show averages in a population whereas the graph on page 29 shows the increase of the world's population. By connecting the tops of the columns in their ThinkMat, students will see a bell-shaped pattern.

If you used a bell-shaped curve to describe giraffe necks, the shortest giraffe necks would be on the opposite end of the curve from the longest. Long-necked giraffes may be at a disadvantage when drinking water in an area with low trees.

After examining the birth by weight graph, students will see that a newborn baby would most likely weigh about 3,000–3,499 g.

This is a good time to distribute ThinkMat 8.

31

Closer to Home: That competitive edge

Have students list some examples of competitive situations (sports, science fairs, talent shows, and so on) and discuss the goal of each one. Then discuss the meaning of the term *competitive advantage*. Help students see that competitive advantages can help individuals and species survive and produce more offspring.

After examining the photograph and reading the caption on page 33, students may suggest that a shorter

basketball player might be able to steal and pass the ball more easily between taller players.

- Since they can grow without soil (and are not restricted to the ground) they would have an advantage in the competition for sunlight.

- The plant species would quickly become extinct.

- The plants with the sweetest nectar and the brightest flowers would probably have a competitive edge.

8 How Do Members of a Population Differ and Compete?

▲ An orchid growing in a rain forest competes for sunlight with other plant species. It also competes for sunlight with members of its own species.

Closer to Home:
That competitive edge

You've probably noticed that there are times when you can move faster or think faster than usual. You win races in the school yard or raise your hand first to answer questions in class. Maybe you ate well or got a really good night's sleep. Maybe you're particularly happy. Whatever the reason, you're on top of the world. You have a competitive edge.

There's more to competition than the kind you're used to at school. Animals and plants compete, too—but in very different ways.

They may compete for food, territory, and mates. Species compete with other species—such as the two kinds of paramecia in Lesson 7. Members of a species also compete with one another.

The faster a cheetah can run, the better its chances of bringing down an antelope for dinner. The better its chances of eating well, the longer the cheetah is likely to survive and reproduce.

- Look at the photo of the orchid at the top of the page. What competitive edge does a rain forest plant with roots that do not need soil have over plants on the rain forest floor?

- What do you think would happen to a plant species with members that didn't live long enough to reproduce?

- Many plants compete to mate. Bees are attracted by sweetness and bright colors. What kinds of plants have a competitive edge in the mating game that bees play with flowers?

Diverse perspectives

Customs of people living on the Trobriand Islands, which are part of Papua, New Guinea, are a good example of cooperation as a competitive trait. Trobrianders have a system of trading with shells, which takes the place of money. What's unusual about the trading system is that people don't try to accumulate wealth. They're expected to pass on what they receive. It's considered a great honor to receive a valuable shell and then give it to someone else. The rules of shell trading are complex. To abide by the rules, people have to move about from island to island. In the process, they're able to get a wide variety of foods and other goods. In this way resources are distributed to the hundreds of communities on the islands. Trobrianders are expected to share the food they grow, too. When a village's food pile is large enough, they throw a party, and everyone in the village gets to share the food. Cooperation serves as a way to keep the community strong.

This is a good opportunity to have students share data and ideas about how cooperation can give them the competitive edge.

◄ Height would appear to give a basketball player a clear competitive edge. What might give a competitive edge to a shorter player?

Think!

Humans cooperate as well as compete to get things done. How might cooperation give one species a competitive advantage over another species?

Think!

Have students list ways humans cooperate with one another—such as living in communities and raising children—and ways they compete—such as for resources, jobs, food, and living space. Cooperation can give one species a competitive advantage because the group uses the ideas and resources of many people rather than depending on an individual.

LESSON THINKING SKILLS:
Interpreting Graphs; Recognizing Patterns and Relationships

33

Assessment Options

Using Students' Process Performance and Recorded Observations

Written Options

1. Students' responses on their LabMat and ThinkMat should give you a clear idea of their understanding of the lesson concept. Use Student Benchmarks to analyze their answers.

2. Have students write about any type of competition they've participated in, such as a spelling bee, a sport, or a science fair. What types of skills or traits were advantageous for the competition?

Oral Options

Listen to students as they do the Exploration. Student Benchmarks will give you an idea of how well they understand the lesson concept.

1. Ask students if they observe other differences among the peanuts aside from size. Are all the textures and colors similar?

2. How students answer the Think question and interpret the bell-shaped graph will also give you a good idea of their understanding of the lesson concept.

The following questions can also be used to assess understanding of the lesson concept:

3. What types of competitive advantages do you have that help you to survive? *(Students may suggest their intelligence, health, ability to get along well with others, and so on.)*

4. How might red fish have a competitive advantage over gray fish of the same species? How might they be at a disadvantage? *(The red fish might attract mates more easily because of their color, but they might also attract more predators.)*

5. What are some examples of cooperative behavior that you've observed within animal species? *(Students may mention the way flocks of birds or herds of animals collectively watch for predators, or the way ants build anthills together and collect food for the colony.)*

Student Benchmarks

Proficient: Students sort and measure peanuts, and see the variations within a species. They explain how such variations can help some members of the species compete successfully against others.

Apprentice: Students identify variations within a species and name some competitive advantages.

Novice: Students identify differences within a species, but may not understand how certain traits are more advantageous.

Portfolio

Student may decide they want to include the LabMat from this lesson in their Portfolio. In addition, they may want to include the Written Option from above.

Reteaching the Novice

Explain to students that scientists compile data on different members of a population and then usually graph the information. The bell-shaped curve that emerges shows the traits that are dominant in a population. Display some examples of bell-shaped graphs. Ask students to identify the top of the curve and the two extremes of the curve for each graph. What does the top of the curve represent? What do the left and right sides of the bell represent? Have students name other variations that could be used in a bell-shaped graph. How do you think this type of graph can help scientists in their research?

Integrating Your Curriculum

INTEGRATING MATH: STATISTICS

Exploring Other Variations

CHALLENGE · CHALLENGE

Have students take a sample of a daisy population (a bunch of daisies) and graph the variability in that population. Tell them to count the petals on each daisy and to keep a careful record of the number of petals on each flower. They should note in particular the smallest and greatest number of petals and take the average. Afterwards, ask them to plot a graph with daisy #1, daisy #2, etc. on the *X* axis and each flower's petal number on the *Y* axis. The graph will be a bell curve. Discuss with students the variability of traits in any population, and let them speculate on what the competitive advantage of having abundant petals might be.

CONNECTING TO LIFE SCIENCE

Competitive Advantages

Have students choose their favorite animal and write a detailed description of it, identifying characteristics that make it unique. If it's an animal students can observe firsthand, have them take field notes. Then have them write a hypothesis about what competitive advantages these characteristics might offer. For example, cats have retractable claws and sharp teeth; they're quick, can slip through small places, and leap high; they can climb trees; their retinas are reflective, which allows them to see well in the dark; and they can use the width of their whiskers to determine whether they'll fit through a space. All these traits might contribute to their being good hunters and being able to defend themselves or escape predators. Have students conduct research about their pets to confirm their hypotheses and add to their understanding. Allow class time for students to present their ideas.

INTEGRATING SOCIAL STUDIES: DRAWING CONCLUSIONS

Nations Compete and Cooperate

Homework Option

Nations cooperate when they work together toward a common goal, such as nuclear disarmament or free trade. Too often, however, they compete with each other for land or power. Ask students to research other examples of the ways nations cooperate and compete. What are the advantages and disadvantages of each example to individual members of the population? to the population (nation) as a whole? Ask students to write a paragraph on their research. Have a world map available so that students can point to the countries as they present their findings to the class.

CURIOSITY PLACE

Competition within a population can be fierce. For example, in one population of 60,000 young Scotch pines, only 1,000 survived to maturity.

How Are Traits Passed From Parents to Offspring?

Lesson Road Map

In the last lesson: Students observed how members of a population differ and compete.

In this lesson: Students demonstrate in a game how traits are passed from parents to offspring.

In the next lesson: Students will play a game to observe how artificial selection can result in desirable traits among offspring.

The Story Line

Grade Level Concept
Different species have inhabited the earth at different times.

Subconcepts
Fossils provide evidence that many species that once inhabited the earth have become extinct.

Changes in the environment or human intervention can result in changes in the characteristics of a population, which are passed on to succeeding generations.

Variation and natural selection have resulted in the evolution of new species.

Lesson Concept
Traits are passed from parents to offspring through genes.

Getting Organized

This lesson requires one 50-minute session.

Materials per Group:

2 coins
Paper
Scissors
Marker
Tape
LabMat 9

Advance Preparation:
Gather materials.

ALSO FOR THIS LESSON:

ThinkMat 9

Thinking activity about the lesson

LabMat 9

Recording sheet for the Exploration

Content Background

There's a vast potential for diversity within most populations. Just think about genetic heredity and sexual reproduction, the phenomenon of genetic mutation, and the effects of the environment. All these factors make for astounding variety in the world.

Through structures called genes, the traits of organisms are passed from parents to offspring. In sexual reproduction offspring inherit genes from both parents. In asexual reproduction, which is common in simpler forms of life such as amebas, the genes of the offspring are identical to those of the parent.

Sometimes there is an identifiable alteration within a gene, called a mutation. Mutations are often associated with inherited diseases, but many scientists believe that mutations are the chief mechanism for evolution and for the development of new species.

The appearance and behavior of an organism are the result of both its inherited and its acquired traits. Acquired traits develop out of an organism's interactions with the environment and are influenced by factors such as nutrition, climate, geography, and socialization. The distinction between inherited and acquired traits is often blurry. For instance, almost anyone can acquire musical ability through study, but are there genetic factors that can explain the amazing Bach family?

Vocabulary

genes: Cell parts that determine many of an organism's traits, including most of its physical traits.

mutation: A change in an organism's genes that can be passed on to the next generation of organisms.

Teachers' Bookshelf

Attenborough, David. *The Living Planet: A Portrait of the Earth.* Boston: Little, Brown, 1986.

Shell, Ellen Ruppel. "Waves of Creation." *Discover.* May 1993, pp. 54–62.

Theme Connection: Patterns of Change

In organisms that reproduce sexually, the combining of genes from two parents results in differences among offspring. When two colors in a visible light spectrum combine—such as in a rainbow—a new color is formed.

Considering Second-Language Learners

Have students work in groups of three or four to play "Who Am I?" Write the following sentences on the chalkboard: My hair is like my [name of family member]. My voice is like my [name of family member]. My eyes are like my [name of family member]. To make this activity diverse, you could use magazines like *Life, Ebony,* or *People* that contain photographs of families. Adjust the sentences accordingly to make comparisons, such as: The girl's hair is just like her mother's.

Naive Conceptions

Students may think that offspring look just like their parents. This lesson shows that in fact there is much genetic variation within families.

LESSON 9

What do we know?
What do we want to know?

1

ACTIVATE

Materials per Group: 2 coins, paper, scissors, marker, tape, LabMat 9

Suggested Grouping: pairs

Approximate Time: 15 minutes

Classroom Management: Copy LabMat 9. Have students take turns tossing the coins.

EXPLORATION:
Make a model of a cat family.

Process Skills and Objectives

Students will:

- **communicate** how offspring resemble their parents

- **compare** traits of parents and their offspring and among offspring

- **predict** types of traits that may be passed on from parents to offspring

- **categorize** traits as acquired or inherited

Opening the Discussion

Ask students: **What physical traits do you think children inherited from their parents?** (*Encourage students to see that traits such as height, eye and hair color, and hair texture are some inherited traits.*) **Can you think of any traits that may not be inherited?** (*Help students to see that certain skills, such as drawing or writing, are learned and develop over time.*)

Have students brainstorm other inherited and acquired traits. Make a list for each on the Recording Board. Then have students read the opening paragraph on page 34.

**Student
Pages 34–35**

LESSON 9

How Are Traits Passed From Parent to Offspring?

You've seen that the members of a population are different from each other in small ways. Even though the differences are small, they can give some members of a population a better chance of staying alive. If those members reproduce, some of their offspring will have these differences, too. How do you think a parent passes these differences—or traits—to its offspring?

Exploration:
Make a model of a cat family.

You need:
Coins
Paper
Scissors
Marker
Tape
LabMat 9

❶ Trace one coin four times on a sheet of paper. Mark three of the circles *X* and the other circle *Y*. Cut them out.

❷ Tape an *X* on both sides of one coin. This coin represents the mother cat. Paste an *X* on one side of the second coin and a *Y* on the other side. This coin represents the father cat.

❸ A kitten needs two parents. Each parent passes some traits to the kitten. One trait is whether the kitten will be male or female. Flip each coin to find out what the first kitten will be. A kitten with two *X*'s will be a female. A kitten with an *X* and a *Y* will be male. Record the result on the LabMat.

❹ Flip the coins again to determine whether the second kitten will be male or female.

❺ Imagine that during her life a mother cat gives birth to 20 kittens. How could you use the coins to predict how many kittens will be male? **Try it.**

Interpret your results.

- What percentage of your cat family was female? male?

- Compare your results with other groups'. What was the percentage of females and males in the whole class?

- Animals inherit traits from both parents, but some traits are determined by only one parent. Which parent determines whether a kitten is born male or female?

EXPLORATION:
Make a model of a cat family.

❷ After distributing LabMat 9, ask students: **Do you think this game shows the passing along of an inherited or an acquired trait?** *(Students will probably realize the game shows the passing down of inherited traits.)*

❹ Ask students to think of other traits that cat parents might pass along to their kittens, such as eye and hair coloring, length of hair, and so on. **Do you think this game can be used to model another species?** *(Students*

will probably realize that the game can be applied to a number of different species.)

❺ Have one student toss the coins while the other records the results.

Interpret Your Results

- Answers will vary, but most will probably be around 50 percent.
- The larger the sample, the closer the answer will be to 50 percent.
- The male cat determines whether the kitten is born male or female.

◀ Even though these kittens look very different, they inherited all of their traits from the same two parents.

▶ A cat with a mutation

Exploration Connection:
Interpreting photographs

Every trait you observed in the cat family is controlled by a special set of chemicals in the cells of their bodies. These chemicals are called <u>genes</u>. When living things reproduce, genes are passed from the parents to the offspring. The genes serve as growing instructions for a developing organism, and they stay in the cells of the organism for its entire life.

Sometimes genes can change before they are passed down. When a gene is changed, its instructions change, too. Once this happened to a gene that controls the number of toes on a kitten's paw. Some kittens were born with something extra—at least one extra toe. This is an example of a <u>mutation</u>, a change in an organism's genes that can be passed on to its offspring. This mutation did not hurt the kittens or shorten their lives. Some people think these cats have better mouse-catching skills!

Mutations happen from time to time in all species of living things. When they happen, they can be passed on. If the mutation gives members of a population a competitive advantage, the character of the entire species can begin to change.

Exploration Connection:
Interpreting photographs

Help students to see that some mutations can introduce a trait that may increase the competitive advantage of a species. In other cases mutations can be a disadvantage (for example, diseases such as Huntington's and sickle-cell anemia).

After looking at the photograph, ask students: **What type of mutation does the cat have?** *(Students will probably notice the extra toes.)* **How might a cat with extra toes have a competitive edge over other four-toed cats?** *(They might be able to catch prey better or grasp for safety more quickly.)*

This is a good time to distribute ThinkMat 9.

35

Closer to Home: Were you born that way?

Have students make their own lists of traits that they've inherited and acquired. They'll probably realize that many skills develop with practice and aren't inherited.

Ask students to think about the question in the caption on page 36. They may suggest that traits such as size or bone structure may enable them to be better ball players.

- Answers might include turning over, crawling, and walking—though each of these requires some learning.

- Because we acquire so much information during our lifetime, it's sometimes hard to distinguish between inherited traits and acquired traits.

- It means that some people may find it impossible to learn to roll their tongue.

9 How Are Traits Passed From Parent to Offspring?

Closer to Home:
Were you born that way?

Like every living organism, you have genes. You know that you inherited these genes and the traits they control. But you also know that you've picked up a great deal from your surroundings. How do people turn out the way they do? Which is more important—the traits we're born with, or the ones we learn? People have been arguing about these questions for a long time.

Sometimes you can tell the difference between a trait you inherited and a trait you learned or acquired some other way. Some traits are always inherited. Unless you wear tinted contact lenses, you inherited everything about your eye color. But you weren't born with a craving for chili or frozen yogurt. If you like these foods, you learned to like them. What about learning to play the piano? If you practice enough, will your children need any lessons at all?

◄ It takes a lot of practice and skill to play baseball well. Are there any traits you could inherit that would make you a better ball player?

Student Pages 36–37

36 SUBCONCEPT TWO: HOW MEMBERS OF SPECIES CHANGE

Diverse perspectives

Sometimes genes passed from parents to offspring carry genetic diseases. One such disease is Huntington's disease, a severe hereditary disorder of the nervous system that destroys brain cells and causes involuntary body movements and mental disturbances.

Nancy Wexler, a clinical psychologist, won the Albert Lasker Public Service Award—the highest honor in American medicine—for her work researching Huntington's disease and for increasing public awareness of all genetic diseases. She helped the effort by collecting hundreds of blood samples from people with the disease in the Lake Maracaibo region of Venezuela, the area with the highest concentration of people with Huntington's disease in the world. She also organized six laboratories in the United States, England, and Wales. The labs cooperated with one another for ten years to find the defective gene that causes the disease. Thanks to Wexler's work, a blood test can accurately predict if someone will get the disease.

This would be a good opportunity to have students get on-line to share data and ideas about acquired traits and inherited traits.

▲ When Judit Polgar was 15, she became the youngest grand master chess champion in the world. Both of her sisters are top-ranked chess players, too.

Neat handwriting, a broken leg, the ability to play piano—these things don't change your genes. So you can't inherit them either—they are called acquired traits. On the other hand, you might have inherited good hand-eye coordination or a very good ear for pitch and rhythm. You've probably heard about musical families: the parents sing, the children play instruments, and everyone can carry a tune. Genes probably play a big part in families like these. But members of these families must also practice long and hard, and in spite of what they might say, none of them were born knowing how to play the cello.

Here are a few questions on the subject you can ask yourself right now:

- What were you born knowing how to do?

- Some inherited traits don't appear at birth, but show up as you grow up. Why does this make it more difficult to tell inherited traits from acquired traits?

- Can you roll your tongue into the shape of the letter *U*? This is an inherited ability. What does that mean about trying to teach it to your friends? **Try it!**

You have inherited many traits. Does that make you less of an individual? Why or why not?

Help students understand that each person is unique— even an identical twin. You can acquire many abilities during your lifetime.

LESSON THINKING SKILLS:
Recognizing Patterns and Relationships; Formulating Questions

37

Assessment Options

Using Students' Process Performance and Recorded Observations

Written Options

1. Students' responses on their LabMat and ThinkMat should give you a clear idea of their understanding of the lesson concept. Use Student Benchmarks to analyze their answers.

2. In addition, have students make a chart showing the results of the Exploration.

Student Benchmarks

Proficient: Students discuss that each parent contributes biological traits to offspring and that acquired traits are learned. They'll realize that some variations may be mutations that can be beneficial to the evolution of a species.

Apprentice: Students discuss the differences between biological traits and acquired traits and can identify how some traits are more advantageous than others.

Novice: Students discuss traits that are passed down from parents to offspring but may not be able to distinguish between inherited and acquired traits.

Portfolio

Students may decide they want to include the LabMat from this lesson in their Portfolio. In addition, they may want to include an Option from page 75.

Oral Options

Listen to students as they do the Exploration. Student Benchmarks will give you an idea of how well they understand the lesson concept.

1. Ask students questions about traits that are inherited and traits that are acquired. Have them name some traits with competitive advantages or disadvantages for a particular athletic game.

2. How students answer the Think question will also give you a good idea of their understanding of the lesson concept.

The following questions can also be used to assess understanding of the lesson concept:

3. Two black-and-white spotted dogs produce a litter of puppies, several of which are tan. What might this suggest about earlier generations of this canine family? *(There must have been some different-colored individuals in the family.)*

4. A mutation in a gene causes a species of insect to produce some offspring that are lighter in color than others. The light-colored offspring are easier for predator birds to see and catch. Do you think this species of insect will continue producing light-colored offspring? Why or why not? *(The lighter-colored offspring may be eaten before they get a chance to reproduce and pass on their genes.)*

Reteaching the Novice

Bring in photographs of human families and/or animal families. Ask students to make two lists—one for the similarities among family members and one for the differences. Then have students identify whether the similarities represent acquired or inherited traits. Ask students to explain their reasoning.

Integrating Your Curriculum

CONNECTING TO LIFE SCIENCE

Mutation and DNA

Explain to students that information on how your body develops is contained in your cells—particularly, in the DNA. DNA is passed from parents to children. It comes in long double strands with rungs between them. They look like ladders, except they are twisted into a helix like a spiral staircase. DNA is made of building blocks of substances called nucleotides. The sequence of the nucleotides determines what the organism will be like. Human DNA is a ladder millions of nucleotides long, and is still so tiny it fits in the center of a single cell. When a mutation occurs, one of these nucleotides is changed in shape.

Materials: 113 g (4 oz) modeling clay

Give each pair of students a 113-g (4 oz) piece of modeling clay.

Have them make models of nucleotides out of the clay (they may simply be small balls or lumps of clay) and put them together to make a strand of DNA with a few twists in it.

Then have them "mutate" a gene by twisting or pinching a single nucleotide. Discuss with students the impact of such mutations: They can be helpful in evolution; they can be harmless; or they can be harmful, as in the case of sickle-cell anemia.

INTEGRATING REFERENCE BOOKS

Animal Behavior

To explore the question of how much behavior is learned and how much is inherited, have students research and write a short narrative about an interesting animal behavior such as birdsong. Rich areas of study include whale and dolphin communication, animal navigation (especially in birds, whales, and dolphins), and animal architects and artists (beavers, spiders, the bowerbirds of Australia, and so on). Have students make illustrations for their narratives and then share them.

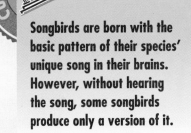

Songbirds are born with the basic pattern of their species' unique song in their brains. However, without hearing the song, some songbirds produce only a version of it.

What Is Artificial Selection?

Student Pages 38–41

Lesson Road Map

In the last lesson: Students demonstrated in a game how traits are passed from parents to offspring.

In this lesson: Students play a game to observe how artificial selection can result in desirable traits among offspring.

In the next lesson: Students will explore the process of natural selection.

The Story Line

Grade Level Concept
Different species have inhabited the earth at different times.

Subconcepts
Fossils provide evidence that many species that once inhabited the earth have become extinct.

Changes in the environment or human intervention can result in changes in the characteristics of a population, which are passed on to succeeding generations.

Variation and natural selection have resulted in the evolution of new species.

Lesson Concept
By selecting animals or plants with certain traits for breeding stock, people have produced new varieties.

Getting Organized

This lesson requires one 50-minute session.

Materials per Group:
Number cube
Paper
Pencil

Advance Preparation:
Gather materials.

ALSO FOR THIS LESSON:

ThinkMat 10
Reviewing the subconcepts

LabMat 10
Recording sheet for the Exploration

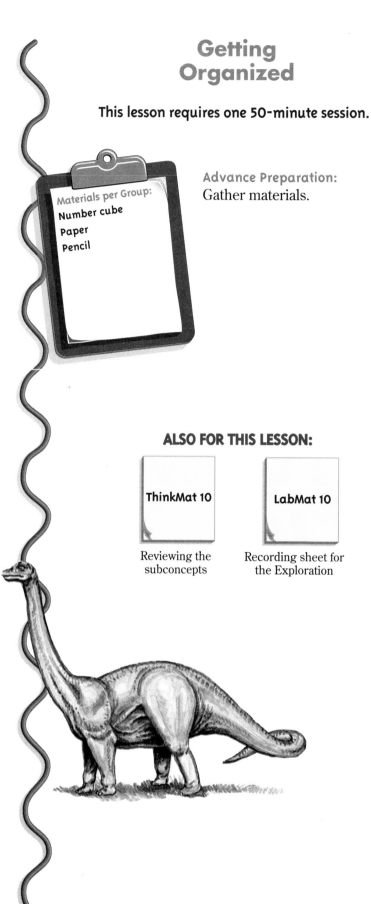

Content Background

Artificial selection is the process by which humans breed a plant or animal species for specific desirable traits. Let's say you wanted to breed sheep for wool. You would select the ewes with the most wool and mate them with the wooliest rams. Many of their offspring would carry the traits of the parents. In each generation you would only mate the sheep that meet your standards.

Artificial selection is the reason we have such a wide variety of fruits and vegetables to choose from. Just think of the different kinds of apples, oranges, and lettuces you've eaten. Most closely related food crops were developed from a single species. For example, cabbage, broccoli, kohlrabi, cauliflower, and brussels sprouts all are a part of the same single species.

As this lesson demonstrates, people can control genetic inheritance to enhance desirable variations within a species. What students may not see in this activity are the real drawbacks of artificial selection. The breeder benefits, but the species doesn't. Genes are so numerous and so profoundly interconnected that breeders can't select them in isolation. For example, the fast rabbits in the activity may have a whole strip of genes right next to the "fast" genes that make them deaf and anemic. So the faster rabbits may look great at the races, but they probably wouldn't survive in a meadow for more than a generation or two.

Variation in offspring is the key to artificial selection. If the next generation of baby rabbits or hens or goldfish merely inherited the exact genes of their parents, a breeder wouldn't have a selection to choose from.

Vocabulary

artificial selection: The breeding of plants or animals with desirable traits to make certain future generations of the organism have the same traits.

Theme Connection: Patterns of Change

Artificial selection is planned and engineered by people as a way of controlling the world's resources to meet human needs. Similarly, people have developed technology, such as the fax machine, to improve worldwide communication.

Considering Second-Language Learners

Have students play this rabbit game in pairs. Read aloud the first paragraph and then demonstrate with one pair how to execute the instructions. Then have one pair act as leaders by having them stand in front of the class to play the game. In each pair, one student will read aloud one sentence at a time, and the other will perform the instruction being read. Have each pair of students compare their results with those of the other pairs. Encourage discussion with simple questions, such as: Who had similar results? different results? Why are your results similar? different? Help students identify some of the similar choices that teams made, which led to similar results.

Naive Conceptions

Students may think that artificial selection is always beneficial to the organisms that are being bred. This lesson shows that it is humans who determine the definition of desirable traits in artificial selection and that problems can arise when organisms are bred for certain traits.

LESSON 10

What do we know?
What do we want to know?

1
ACTIVATE

EXPLORATION:
Make a faster rabbit.

Process Skills and Objectives

Students will:

- **communicate** what they know about inherited traits

- **compare** offspring in order to select the best individuals to breed

Opening the Discussion

Review with students what they learned in the previous lesson about the inheritance of traits that are passed on from one generation to the next. Ask students: **What is the main difference between an inherited trait and an acquired trait?** *(Students will probably recall that acquired traits are learned whereas inherited traits aren't.)*

Ask students to define *artificial*. Have them think of artificial and natural foods that they eat. Write their responses on the Recording Board. Then have students read the first paragraph on page 38.

PREPARING FOR THE EXPLORATION

Materials per Group: number cube, paper, pencil

Suggested Grouping: pairs

Approximate Time: 30 minutes

Classroom Management: Copy LabMat 10. For students who finish the game first, have them do one of the Options on page 83.

LESSON 10

What Is Artificial Selection?

What if you returned to Rabbit Island and started a rabbit ranch? The only problem is those pesky foxes. They'll eat your rabbits right off the island if you don't do something soon. Is there any way to breed a rabbit that can outrun a fox?

Exploration:
Make a faster rabbit.

You need:
Number cube
Paper
Pencil

❶ Start with two rabbits—one male, one female. The female rabbit can run 2 km per hour. The male can run 1 km per hour. Your goal is to breed a rabbit that can run 19 km per hour in as few generations as possible. Each generation has four rabbits.

❷ Roll the number cube. Add this number to the speed of the faster parent. This is the first baby rabbit's speed. Record the speed.

❸ Repeat step 2 for the other three babies. Record all four speeds on your LabMat.

❹ Now the babies have grown. Pick the two fastest rabbits to breed a new generation. Repeat steps 2 and 3 to find the speeds of these rabbits.

❺ Keep selecting the fastest rabbits to breed new generations. Stop playing when you reach your goal.

Interpret your results.

- Breeding plants or animals with desirable traits is called <u>artificial</u> <u>selection</u>. How many generations did it take to breed a rabbit that can run 19 km per hour?

- How would the game have been different if the fastest baby could run only 1 km per hour faster than its parents? **Try it!**

38 SUBCONCEPT TWO: HOW MEMBERS OF SPECIES CHANGE

EXPLORATION: Make a faster rabbit.

2 Make sure students take turns rolling the dice, recording the data, and selecting the fastest rabbit. Distribute LabMat 10.

4 Explain to students that a generation is one step in the line of descent from an ancestor.

5 Ask: **In real life what problems could a breeder encounter?** *(environmental factors and diseases)*

Interpret Your Results

- Answers will vary but will probably be about three or four generations.
- It would take about 17 generations.

Exploration Connection:
Interpreting photographs

Students will probably see from the photographs that lop-eared rabbits are bred as pets for their cuteness. A wild rabbit would need traits such as speed and thicker coats to survive. Students will probably come up with a number of different answers for the traits that a pet rabbit would need, such as a good disposition.

Ask: **Can you think of other species that have been artificially bred by humans? Do you know the reasons why?** *(There will be a variety of answers; make sure students understand the reasons for artificially breeding certain species. For example, cattle may be bred for their meat, apples may be bred for their taste, sheep may be bred for their wool, and so on.)*

The ThinkMat for this lesson is a review of the second subconcept.

Rabbit variations include the Lop-eared rabbit (top), the Snowshoe rabbit (center), and the New Zealand rabbit (bottom).

Exploration Connection:
Interpreting photographs

Raising rabbits as pets is a big business in the United States. Thousands of rabbit lovers in every state breed rabbits for pets, but most rabbits are raised in special places where millions of the future pets are born every year.

Rabbit growers control breeding by keeping males and females apart except when they want them to reproduce. The growers breed the rabbits for different traits, including coat color. The four basic varieties of rabbit coat color are gray, tan pattern, shaded pattern, and albino white.

Some rabbits, such as the angora rabbit, are bred for thick and silky fur. And because many people around the world consider rabbit meat a delicacy, some varieties are bred to be eaten.

Look at the three photos. The New Zealand rabbit is one of several varieties bred to be eaten. Which of the other two rabbits was most likely bred to be a pet? What evidence do you see in the photos to support your idea?

A wild rabbit must have traits that suit its environment. What traits does a wild rabbit need that a pet rabbit doesn't? What traits does a pet rabbit need that a wild rabbit doesn't?

Closer to Home: Who put the pop in popcorn?

Lead a discussion with students about the different kinds of corn they've eaten. Ask: **How was each similar or different? Did the corn taste different because of the way it was prepared?** *(Answers will vary and may include corn on the cob, creamed corn, corn kernels, popcorn, corn fritters, cornmeal mush, and so on. Students will probably describe the different textures and realize that the way corn is prepared changes its texture and taste.)*

- The compact mushroom-shaped popcorn is made from corn that was bred to be popped before it is shipped.

- Corn has been bred for certain characteristics based on popular appeal.

---

10 What Is Artificial Selection?

Closer to Home:
Who put the pop in popcorn?

Can you imagine going to the movies and not eating popcorn? Those fluffy, crunchy, and delicious puffs of corn are the result of artificial selection. So is almost everything you see in the meat and vegetable departments of your supermarket. Most of the food grown today was bred from ancient plants or animals by artificial selection.

That's true for chicken, for broccoli, and for corn. People in the central and southern regions of what is now Mexico gathered and ate corn from wild plants thousands of years ago. The oldest known corncobs are 7,000 years old—and tiny compared to today's ears of corn. The ancient ears of corn were about 2.5 centimeters (1 inch) long and had from 50 to 60 kernels.

The fresh corn that you can buy every summer has a soft yellow or white kernel that tastes sweet. The popcorn you snack on at home and in movie theaters is a different kind of corn. Popcorn kernels have hard shells and range in color from white to orange to blue. The shell surrounds a bit of moist starch, and when the kernel is heated, the moisture changes to steam. The trapped steam makes the shell explode.

Like corn, popcorn is a Native American food. Native Americans on both continents were eating popcorn, decorating with it, and using it in religious ceremonies when European explorers arrived in the fifteenth and sixteenth centuries. Today, the United States produces two fifths of the world's corn and almost all the popcorn.

- Some popcorn pops into small mushroom shapes, and other kinds pop into a large, fluffy butterfly shapes. Which kind of popcorn do you think is bred to be popped before it is shipped?

- Farmers plant far fewer kinds of corn than they did 200 years ago. How could this be a result of artificial selection?

▼ Butter and Sugar is a popular variety of fresh corn.

40 SUBCONCEPT TWO: HOW MEMBERS OF SPECIES CHANGE

Diverse perspectives

Corn was first cultivated by Native Americans thousands of years ago. Archaeologists have found 7,000-year-old fossil corncobs in cave dwellings. Native Americans used artificial selection to create corn that was hardy and produced many seeds. They bred corn to be bigger and to grow a tougher core and longer husks for protection. They also grew many varieties. Some corn was banded, spotted, or striped.

Columbus learned about corn from the Native Americans and introduced it to the Europeans. Native Americans also taught the American colonists how to grow corn. The practice of farming corn spread from its origin in central Mexico all the way north to Canada and all the way south to Chile. Today, corn continues to be a food staple for people throughout the Americas. In Mexico people have been eating corn tortillas—which are used to make tacos and burritos—for centuries.

► Ancient corn is still grown in some parts of the United States.

◄ Silver Queen has been bred for its taste.

Many Americans still decorate their homes with many-colored ears of Indian corn. The three ears here were bred only for decoration.

This would be a good opportunity to have students get on-line to share data and ideas about different crops that are bred in your area.

Think!

What problems might rabbit growers have if they tried to breed faster and faster rabbits?

Think!

Animal breeders can encounter all kinds of problems when they selectively breed for a characteristic such as speed. Sometimes an animal's skeletal structure can't stand the stress of the new speed, or its cardiopulmonary system can be overworked.

LESSON THINKING SKILLS:
Recognizing Relationships; Applying Information to New Situations

41

Assessment Options

Using Students' Process Performance and Recorded Observations

Written Options

1. Students' responses on their LabMat and ThinkMat should give you a clear idea of their understanding of the lesson concept. Use Student Benchmarks to analyze their answers.

2. In addition, have students think about a fruit or vegetable they would want to improve. Ask them to write a paragraph identifying the traits they would want to breed.

Student Benchmarks

Proficient: Students discuss how and why people have produced new varieties of plants and animals through artificial selection, and why certain traits are more desirable than others.

Apprentice: Students demonstrate that producing new varieties of plants or animals involves artificially selecting favorable traits for breeding.

Novice: Students realize that people can artificially produce new varieties of plants and animals but may not understand how or why.

Portfolio

Students may decide they want to include the LabMat from this lesson in their Portfolio. In addition, they may want to include the Written Options from above.

Oral Options

Listen to students as they do the Exploration. Student Benchmarks will give you an idea of how well they understand the lesson concept.

1. Ask students about the types of problems breeders might encounter. Help students realize that climate and environment are crucial for breeding.

2. How students answer the Think and Closer to Home questions will also give you a good idea of their understanding of the lesson concept.

The following questions can also be used to assess understanding of the lesson concept:

3. Why do you think the process in which people breed plants and animals for desirable traits is called artificial? *(People, not nature, control the process.)*

4. What are some traits besides color and taste that a fruit grower might want to improve? *(Perhaps the grower would choose traits such as the ability to resist disease, to grow in different climates or soils, or to thrive on different amounts of water or sunlight.)*

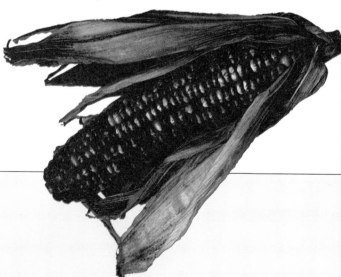

Reteaching the Novice

Bring into class a variety of apples, such as Macintosh, Golden Delicious, and Granny Smith. Ask students to describe how each apple looks—its color, shape, and texture. Then cut the apples into thin slices and allow students to taste a few different types. Ask them to describe the taste of each apple. Ask them to think of reasons for artificially breeding each variety of apple. Write their responses on the chalkboard.

Integrating Your Curriculum

INTEGRATING LANGUAGE ARTS

Hold a Debate

CHALLENGE • CHALLENGE

Have the class select one species that has been bred by humans and make lists of the pros and cons of breeding this species using artificial selection. Then divide the class into two teams and have them present opposing arguments in favor of or in opposition to the artificial selection of that species. An example of a topic of debate might be the breeding of milk cows. One team might argue that it's important for humans to try to create a more productive cow. The other team might argue that artificial selection produces cows that are weaker in other ways and that it's dangerous to risk reducing the gene pool.

INTEGRATING SOCIAL STUDIES: EVALUATING

Charting Grain

SCHOLASTIC NETWORK

For thousands of years, people around the world have practiced artificial selection, attempting to improve the grain crops grown in their areas. Archaeologists have found cultivated wheat grains dating from 7000 B.C. in the Middle East. The people of Asia were growing rice as long as 5,000 years ago. European explorers and settlers found Native Americans raising corn throughout the Americas. Invite students to work in groups to find out more about the history of these and other grains such as barley, rye, and oats. You may also suggest that students use the network to gather ideas from other students. Where were such crops first grown? How have they been changed through artificial selection? How have these changes been good or bad for the crops and the people dependent on them? How is artificial selection being used to improve these grains today? Have groups create a chart that answers such questions for several different kinds of grain.

CONNECTING TO LIFE SCIENCE

Domestic Animals

Homework Option

Domestic animals are usually the result of artificial selection. Have students select a breed of cat or dog and write a hypothesis about the traits the animal was bred for, based on what they know about the animal's appearance and behavior. For example, dachshund were bred to hunt badgers, which accounts for their long bodies and short legs and their desire to burrow. Then have students research the breed they selected and write their findings under the hypothesis. Ask them to contrast these traits with those that might have evolved naturally. For example, a cat might not have developed long fur naturally because it would have been a nuisance in the wild.

CURIOSITY PLACE

The rhino mouse, a product of artificial selection, first develops a normal coat but then loses its hair and becomes wrinkled.

How Are Species Selected Naturally?

Lesson Road Map

In the last lesson: Students played a game to observe how artificial selection can result in desirable traits among offspring.

In this lesson: Students explore the process of natural selection. In Part One they observe how natural selection may affect the survival of a population. In Part Two they observe how certain characteristics help organisms survive.

In the next lesson: Students will investigate ways in which new species may develop.

The Story Line

Grade Level Concept

Different species have inhabited the earth at different times.

Subconcepts

Fossils provide evidence that many species that once inhabited the earth have become extinct.

Changes in the environment or human intervention can result in changes in the characteristics of a population, which are passed on to succeeding generations.

Variation and natural selection have resulted in the evolution of new species.

Lesson Concept

Members of a species that are better adapted to their environment are more likely to survive than members that aren't as well adapted.

Getting Organized

This lesson requires two 45-minute sessions.

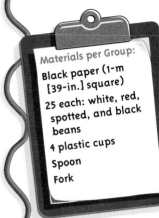

Materials per Group:

Black paper (1-m [39-in.] square)

25 each: white, red, spotted, and black beans

4 plastic cups

Spoon

Fork

PART ONE

Advance Preparation:
In addition to the materials on the clipboard, you'll need a clothespin and a clock or watch with a second hand.

Materials per Group:

ThinkMat 11

Scissors

Pencil or pen

PART TWO

Advance Preparation:
Gather materials.

ALSO FOR THIS LESSON:

ThinkMat 11

For use with the Exploration

LabMats 11A and 11B

Recording sheets for the Exploration

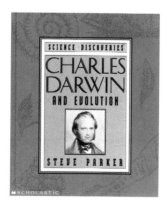

SCIENCE DISCOVERIES
CHARLES DARWIN AND EVOLUTION
STEVE PARKER

Pages 18—22

For Science Browsers

"We Invited Carp to America"
Student page 69

Content Background

The central idea behind natural selection is that there's great variety within a species: No two organisms are exactly alike. Organisms best suited to the rigors of their environment are the most likely to survive and pass their traits to offspring through reproduction. These traits in turn give the offspring an advantage in the environment. In other words, nature selects the most favorable characteristics for survival, and the survivors with these traits pass them to their offspring. In this way, usually over a period of time, a species becomes adapted to its environment.

A change that allows an organism to survive in its environment is called an adaptation. Nature has a vast array of adaptations that allow species to survive the harshest of climates, to camouflage themselves, to mimic, to fly, to defend or to attack, to enhance sexual attraction, and to build shelters. Charles Darwin called these adaptations life's "ever-branching and beautiful ramifications."

Chance also plays a key role in natural selection because genetic variation itself is random. Nature either accepts or rejects variations, which include mutations. If a trait or a mutation proves advantageous to survival and increases the chance that the organism will reproduce, the odds are that the same trait will occur with increased frequency in the next generation.

Vocabulary

natural selection: The tendency over time for the organism best adjusted to an environment to be the most likely to survive and reproduce.

evolution: The scientific theory that groups of organisms change their shape and structure over long periods of time.

Theme Connection: Patterns of Change

When an environment changes, certain species may have traits that are more suited to those changes. Similarly, climatic changes have altered the structure of some of Earth's landforms.

Considering Second-Language Learners

Use the first paragraph of this lesson to help students formulate hypotheses about the examples of natural selection mentioned. They'll also get practice using the past tense in declarative sentences.

Have a volunteer read aloud the first paragraph. Write the last sentence of the paragraph on the chalkboard: "How did this happen?" Tell students to think of as many answers as possible. Encourage them to think of both realistic and fantastic reasons, such as: Polar bears have thick white coats to protect them from the cold and from predators. The first polar bears lost their color in the sun.

Naive Conceptions

Students may think that organisms purposely develop certain adaptations. This lesson shows that organisms don't select their own adaptations. The organisms best suited to their environment are most likely to survive and reproduce.

LESSON 11 **Part One**

What do we know?
What do we want to know?

1

ACTIVATE

EXPLORATION:
May the best eater win.

Process Skills and Objectives

Students will:

- **observe** that organisms have certain traits that help them survive in their environment

- **communicate** how natural selection allows individuals with certain traits to survive in their environment

- **compare** traits within a species to understand which traits favor survival in a particular environment

Opening the Discussion

Have students read the first paragraph on page 42. Encourage students to think of different animals and plants and their habitats, such as a chameleon in forest foliage, a clam on a beach, or a cactus in a desert.

Ask students: **What traits do these organisms have that give them an advantage in their environment?** *(Chameleons are able to change color; clams have hard shells; and cactus have structures that enable them to absorb and store water.)* Record students' responses on the Recording Board.

PREPARING FOR THE EXPLORATION

Materials per Group: black paper (1-m [39-in.] square); 25 each: white, red, spotted, and black beans; 4 plastic cups; spoon; fork; clothespin; timer or clock with second hand

Suggested Grouping: four

Approximate Time: 25 minutes

Classroom Management: Copy LabMat 11A. You could jigsaw this lesson by assigning the Explorations on pages 42 and 44 to different groups to do at the same time. Then have them share their results.

LESSON 11

How Are Species Selected Naturally?

Humans are responsible for melt-in-your-mouth popcorn, but they didn't have anything to do with the polar bear's thick white coat or the tiny hummingbird's incredibly fast-beating wings. Most species' traits developed long before people began using artificial selection. How did this happen?

Exploration
May the best eater win.

You need:

Black paper
25 each white,
red, spotted,
and black
beans
4 plastic cups

Spoon
Fork
Clothespin
Clock or watch
with second
hand

❶ Mix all the beans together. Then spread them out evenly on the black paper.

❷ Imagine you are a predator. The beans are your prey. The cup is your stomach. Three students choose a spoon, fork, or clothespin for capturing prey. (No fair using hands!)

❸ In one minute, capture as many beans as possible and put them into your cup. Record the number and kind of beans you captured. ✎

❹ What was the average number of beans captured by your team? If you captured fewer than the average number of beans captured, you're out. ✎

❺ If you're not out, play another round with the remaining players. Record your data again. ✎

Interpret your results.

- Which predator ate the most prey? Which ate the least prey? Why did some predators starve?

- Which color of prey was eaten most? Which color was eaten least? Why?

- What do predators and prey each need to survive and reproduce?

EXPLORATION: May the best eater win.

Troubleshooting: Students who are color-blind should work closely with other group members in this Exploration.

2 Ask one member of each group to act as timekeeper. Distribute LabMat 11A.

4 Have students describe how difficult each object is to use.

5 Help students make the connection between adaptations and environments. Have students think of ways other than color that plants and animals seem well suited to their environments. For example, what adaptations are useful for moving around in water?

Interpret Your Results

- Answers will vary; the spoon probably ate the most prey and the clothespin the least. Some predators starved when they didn't get enough beans.

- Answers will vary, but probably the white. Black beans survived the best because they were the same color as the paper.

- Predators need a good way to catch prey, and prey need speed or a good camouflage.

Exploration Connection:
Using reference books

You've seen how color affects your ability to see beans and pick them up quickly. So you may not be surprised to discover that a living organism's color can affect its chances of survival.

In England, a species of moth called the peppered moth has two color variations. Peppered moths are either light or dark. Until the mid-1800s, the air in England was clean, and dark peppered moths were very rare. All over England, coal-burning factories were beginning to dirty the air with smoke and soot that darkened cities and nearby woods. For the next 100 years, people saw more dark moths than light moths. The dark color protected these moths from their predators—birds.

▲ In a soot-covered forest, would a hungry bird be more likely to find the light peppered moth (top) or the dark peppered moth?

Though people affected the population of peppered moths by dirtying the air, no one had set out to breed a dark peppered moth. The changes in the populations of peppered moths are an example of a different kind of selection—natural selection. Natural selection means that the organisms that best fit an environment are most likely to survive and reproduce. How does this describe what happened to dark peppered moths?

Charles Darwin's idea of natural selection gave him a foundation for the theory that species change over time. This theory—called evolution—was somewhat dangerous to discuss openly in the mid-1800s. To learn how this idea was brought into the open, turn to pages 18–22 in *Charles Darwin and Evolution*.

Exploration Connection:
Using reference books

From the photographs students will see that in a soot-covered wood, birds would spot light-colored moths more easily. The dark-peppered moths were naturally selected by color.

In *Charles Darwin and Evolution*, students will read about the criticism that Darwin received on his theory of evolution. Ask: **Do you think scientists today are criticized in the same way?** *(Help students to see that scientists probably get criticized often when their ideas drastically change a given theory. Research and observational notes help to convince their critics.)*

43

⑤ Have students think about factors other than speed that could influence the rabbit or fox populations in real life. Ask: **Would some slower rabbits have a survival advantage over others?** *(Some rabbits might have a keener sense of hearing or a color that would camouflage them.)*

EXPLORATION:
Return to Rabbit Island.

Process Skills and Objectives
Students will:

- **observe** how certain traits are selected for breeding

- **compare** what happens to the two different rabbit populations during the game

- **predict** what would happen if all the rabbits were slow or all were fast

PREPARING FOR THE EXPLORATION

Materials per Group: ThinkMat 11, scissors, pencil or pen

Suggested Grouping: four

Approximate Time: 25 minutes

Classroom Management: Copy LabMat 11B. Make sure students are rotating responsibilities.

EXPLORATION:
Return to Rabbit Island.

❶ ❷ After distributing LabMat 11B, ask students to try to relate experiences from the previous games as they play this game.

❸ ❹ If a rabbit lands on the same space as the fox, don't remove any rabbit tokens.

⑥ Troubleshooting: Be sure students remember to mark the tokens that stand for the descendants of each original pair of rabbits.

Student Pages 44–45

---

11 How Are Species Selected Naturally?

You've seen how certain traits—whether they're artificially selected or naturally selected—can affect a species' chance for survival. You know how artificial selection works. But what kind of model can you use to find out how natural selection works?

Exploration:
Return to Rabbit Island.

You need:
LabMat 11B
Scissors
Pencil or pen

❶ Cut out the animal tokens. Place one fox on the F square and four rabbits on the R square. Two rabbits move two spaces each turn, and the other two move one space per turn. Mark two rabbit tokens "2" and mark the other two rabbit tokens "1." ✐

❷ The fox can move up to four spaces each turn, but it can only move far enough to eat. It can't pass the rabbits.

❸ The fox moves first. Each time it catches up with rabbits, it stops to eat. Take one rabbit off the board. Record changes in populations on your LabMat. ✐

❹ The rabbits move second. Both groups of rabbits move forward during each rabbit turn. Each time a group reaches a Breed square, it doubles in number. You mark the new tokens either "1" or "2," depending on which group of rabbits they come from. ✐

❺ Keep playing the game until the rabbits are all eaten up, the fox starves, or the rabbits have gone around the gameboard twice.

Interpret your results.

- How does the rabbit population change during the game?

- What would happen to the rabbit population if all the rabbits were from the slower group?

- What effect would a slower rabbit population eventually have on the fox population?

▲ The fossilized mosquito preserved in amber (above) is the ancestor of the modern pest (right).

44 SUBCONCEPT THREE: HOW NEW SPECIES DEVELOP

Interpret Your Results

• The slower rabbits always get eaten first, so the percentage of fast rabbits in the population continually increases.

• None or very few would survive.

• If the foxes killed all the rabbits, the foxes could eventually starve to death.

Closer to Home: Tough bugs

Encourage students to name some insects that are considered pests (cotton boll weevils, lice, ticks, mites, cockroaches) and others that are considered beneficial (bees, butterflies, ladybugs).

After students have examined the photographs and captions, ask: **Why do you think it was easy for insects to become entrapped in amber?** (*Insects are small enough to become totally entrapped by the tree sap.*)

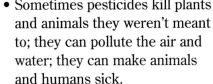

• Sometimes pesticides kill plants and animals they weren't meant to; they can pollute the air and water; they can make animals and humans sick.

This would be a good time to distribute ThinkMat 11.

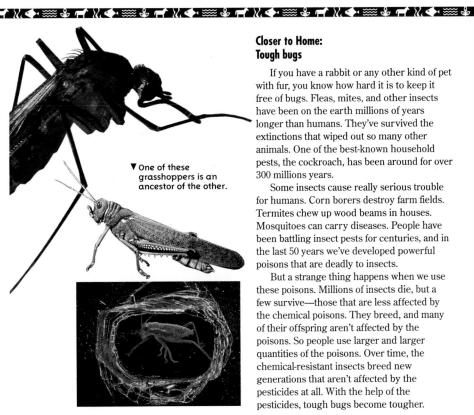

Closer to Home: Tough bugs

If you have a rabbit or any other kind of pet with fur, you know how hard it is to keep it free of bugs. Fleas, mites, and other insects have been on the earth millions of years longer than humans. They've survived the extinctions that wiped out so many other animals. One of the best-known household pests, the cockroach, has been around for over 300 millions years.

Some insects cause really serious trouble for humans. Corn borers destroy farm fields. Termites chew up wood beams in houses. Mosquitoes can carry diseases. People have been battling insect pests for centuries, and in the last 50 years we've developed powerful poisons that are deadly to insects.

But a strange thing happens when we use these poisons. Millions of insects die, but a few survive—those that are less affected by the chemical poisons. They breed, and many of their offspring aren't affected by the poisons. So people use larger and larger quantities of the poisons. Over time, the chemical-resistant insects breed new generations that aren't affected by the pesticides at all. With the help of the pesticides, tough bugs become tougher.

• Besides breeding tougher bugs, what problems do you think people have created with pesticides? List at least three.

▼ One of these grasshoppers is an ancestor of the other.

Think!

Ask students to give examples of natural and artificial selection. People use artificial selection to breed plants and animals for their own specific purposes; the process doesn't improve a species' biological chance of survival as it would in natural selection. Natural selection usually takes place over a long period of time, whereas in artificial selection the process is sped up.

Think!

What is the difference between natural selection and artificial selection?

45

LESSON THINKING SKILLS:
Recognizing Patterns and Relationships; Contrasting; Drawing Conclusions

Assessment Options

Using Students' Process Performance and Recorded Observations

Written Options

1. Students' responses on their LabMats and ThinkMat should give you a clear idea of their understanding of the lesson concept. Use Student Benchmarks to analyze their answers.

2. In addition, have students think about a real-life environment for Exploration One. Then ask them to list some naturally selected traits that would be advantageous for fish in a pond.

Student Benchmarks

Proficient: Students demonstrate that members of a species are more likely to survive and produce offspring when they're better adapted to their environment.

Apprentice: Students demonstrate how certain physical characteristics make some animals more able to adapt to their environment.

Novice: Students discuss that a species must adapt to its environment in order to survive but may not understand how natural selection works.

Portfolio

Students may decide they want to include the LabMats for this lesson in their Portfolio. In addition, they may want to include the Written Options from above.

Oral Options

Listen to students as they do the Explorations. Student Benchmarks will give you an idea of how well they understand the lesson concept.

1. In Part One, ask students to identify other naturally selected traits aside from color that might help an organism survive in the wild.

2. In Part Two, ask students to think of traits aside from speed that might be advantageous to the rabbits or fox. Have them think about the environment and other factors such as natural disasters that might come into play.

3. How students answer the Think question will also give you a good idea of their understanding of the lesson concept.

The following questions can also be used to assess understanding of the lesson concept:

4. Dolphins and tuna fish aren't closely related, yet both have fins and streamlined shapes. How do you think they developed similar forms? *(These adaptations were well suited to an ocean environment and helped both dolphins and tuna survive.)*

5. Suppose the environment of a certain species is suddenly destroyed. What is likely to happen to the species? Why? *(The species is likely to be destroyed because there won't be time for it to develop adaptations to its new environment.)*

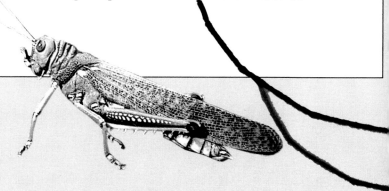

Reteaching the Novice

Bring in photographs of animals and plants in their habitats that seem well adapted to their environment, such as polar bears, snowshoe hares, pine trees, cactuses, and so on. Do the animals or plants have any unique characteristics that make it easier for them to survive in their particular environment? Could the animal or plant exist in that environment without that particular characteristic?

Integrating Your Curriculum

CONNECTING TO LIFE SCIENCE
Adaptation in Plants

Assign or let students choose one of the following habitats: desert, ocean, tundra, savanna, and rain forest. Have them research and write about what the habitats are like and what kinds of plants live there. Ask students to analyze the characteristics that have contributed to the survival of the plants in their habitats. Have students draw their habitats, too.

LONG-TERM CLASS PROJECT
Survival of the Fittest

Provide the class with four potted plants (ones you can dig up rather than buy and that are hardy enough to survive replanting, such as grass or dandelions). Students should place each plant in a different area of the classroom (sunny, partially lighted, dim, and dark). Have them water the plants with the same amount of water every week. As a class, ask students to make a table to monitor the plants' growth or decline. Tell students to note how the colors and textures have changed.

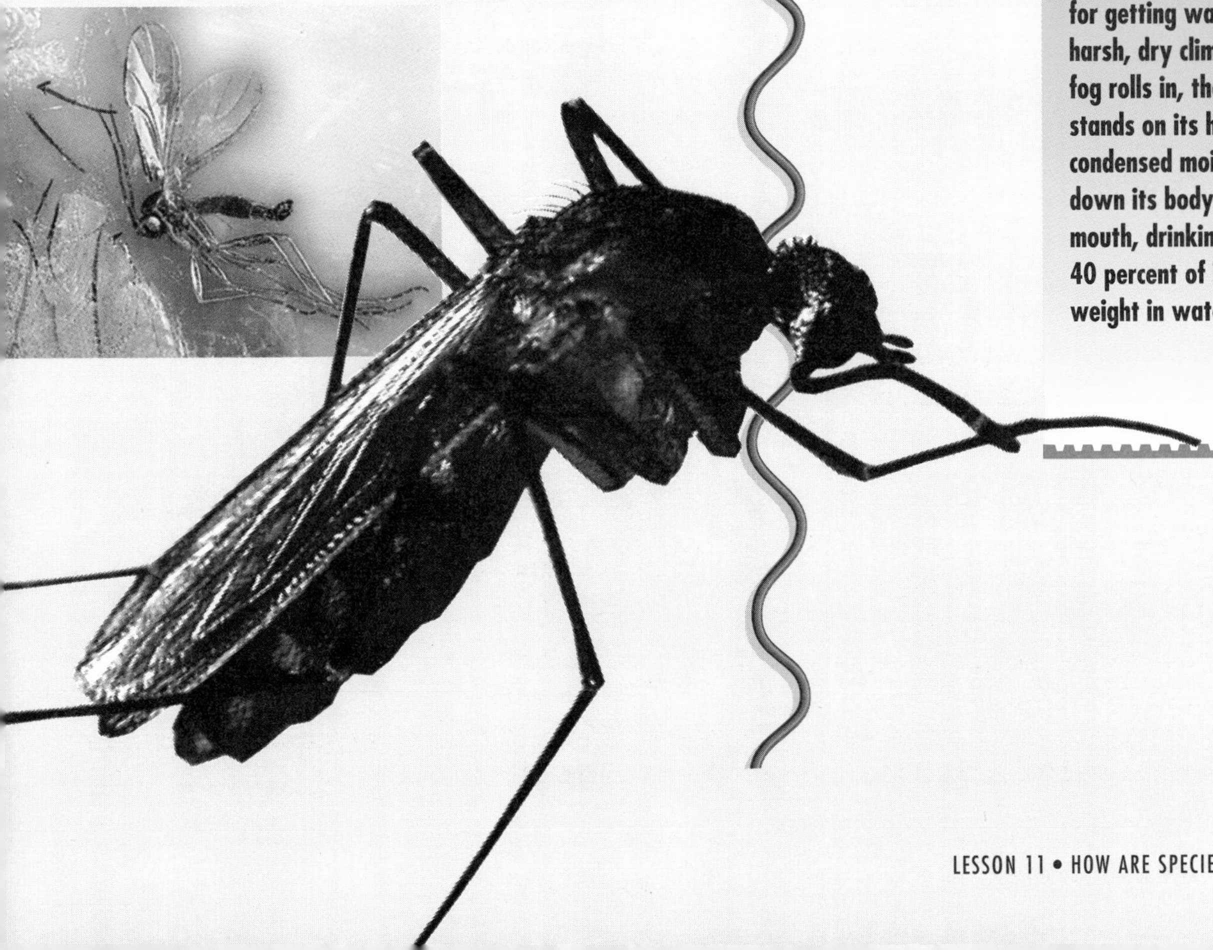

INTEGRATING LANGUAGE ARTS
Nature Journals

Homework Option

Journals can help students develop close observation skills. Have each student start a personal naturalist's or "adventuring-eye" journal for nature observations, writing a paragraph for each observation. Two books about nature that students might enjoy are *A Practical Guide for the Amateur Naturalist* by Gerald Malcolm Durrell and *A Life in Hand: Creating the Illuminated Journal* by Hannah Hinchmann. Ask students to focus on notes and drawings instead of collecting actual specimens.

CURIOSITY PLACE

The African darkling beetle has an unusual adaptation for getting water in a harsh, dry climate. When fog rolls in, the beetle stands on its head and lets condensed moisture roll down its body toward its mouth, drinking as much as 40 percent of its body weight in water.

How Could New Species Develop?

Lesson Road Map

In the last lesson: Students explored the process of natural selection.

In this lesson: Students investigate ways in which new species may develop.

In the next lesson: Students will explore the structural similarities between living species.

Getting Organized

This lesson requires one 45-minute session.

Materials per Group:
None

Advance Preparation: none

The Story Line

Grade Level Concept
Different species have inhabited the earth at different times.

Subconcepts
Fossils provide evidence that many species that once inhabited the earth have become extinct.

Changes in the environment or human intervention can result in changes in the characteristics of a population, which are passed on to succeeding generations.

Variation and natural selection have resulted in the evolution of new species.

Lesson Concept
Changes resulting from variation and selection can lead to the evolution of new species.

ALSO FOR THIS LESSON:

ThinkMat 12

Thinking activity about the lesson

For Science Browsers

"Excerpt from *The Life and Letters of Charles Darwin*" Student page 68

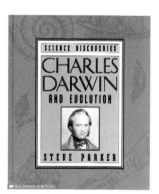

SCIENCE DISCOVERIES
CHARLES DARWIN AND EVOLUTION
STEVE PARKER

Pages 8–14

Content Background

A species is a group of organisms with common characteristics that can breed with one another and produce viable offspring (that is, offspring that can also mate and produce young). Speciation—the formation of a new species—may occur when natural selection brings about changes that either completely transform one species into another or split one species into a number of separate species. Of the two processes, the latter, "species splitting," represents the main dynamic of evolution.

New species may evolve as a species responds and adapts to changing conditions in its environment. For example, groups within one population of a species may become separated by a geographical barrier, such as a sea or a mountain range. Though the groups could still interbreed, the barrier prevents them from doing so. The separate groups may now be in different environments as well. Over time, each becomes adapted to its new environment. If the adaptations produce such great differences between the groups that they can no longer interbreed, the genetic continuity between them is broken and they split into separate species. This is what happened to the Galápagos finches, which students will read about in this lesson.

Scientists today believe that species formation may occur in jerks and twitches rather than smoothly and gradually, as Darwin believed. In certain cases it may only take tens of thousands of years, a short span in geological time, for a new species to form, instead of millions of years.

Vocabulary

adaptation: A trait that lets an organism compete successfully in an environment.

Teachers' Bookshelf

Gould, Stephen Jay. *Ever Since Darwin: Reflections in Natural History.* New York: Norton, 1979.

Miller, Jonathan, and Borin Van Loon. *Darwin for Beginners.* New York: Pantheon, 1982.

Theme Connection: Patterns of Change

Changes resulting from variation and selection can lead to the evolution of new species. Similarly, changes in Earth's crust can lead to the development of new landforms.

Considering Second-Language Learners

For this activity, it would be a good idea to pair second-language learners with more proficient students or fluent English speakers. Review the ideas about where the first vertebrate land animals came from. Ask students to choose a pet or a familiar animal and draw it. This will be the "original" species. Then encourage them to imagine how the species might develop differently if there was a dramatic change in its environment or climate. Tell them to transform the original into three other species. Ask them to write short captions for each picture, describing the physical characteristics and how they differ from the original species.

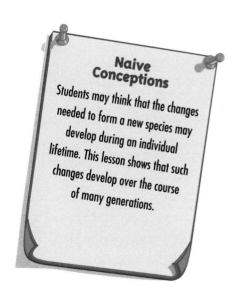

Naive Conceptions

Students may think that the changes needed to form a new species may develop during an individual lifetime. This lesson shows that such changes develop over the course of many generations.

LESSON 12

What do we know?
What do we want to know?

1
ACTIVATE

Thinking Skills and Objectives

Students will:

- **recognize cause-and-effect relationships** between adaptation and the development of new species

- **communicate** the patterns and relationships that a changing environment can have on the development of new species

Opening the Discussion

Have students think about two different-looking fruits, such as a coconut and a banana. Tell students to imagine that they live on an island where these two fruits are the only food sources. Have them consider the type of physical adaptations animals would need for such a diet. Ask: **Would they need a strong set of teeth and jaws to eat the coconut, or agile hands and fingers to peel the banana? Would they need any special ability to get at the food, such as the strength to open the hard shell of the coconut or the nimbleness to climb a tall tree to get the bananas?** (*Accept all answers that show students are using logical reasoning skills.*)

Help students think about what might happen if one of the food sources disappeared. **What might happen to the animals that depended on the food?** (*Students will probably realize that some of the animals might die.*) Write their responses on the Recording Board.

**Student
Pages 46–47**

Diverse perspectives

The Galápagos Islands, once known as the Enchanted Isles, are part of Ecuador. The name "Galápagos" comes from the Spanish word for turtle. Huge turtles weighing more than 230 km (500 lb) and marine lizards about 1.25 m (4 ft) long share the island with other exotic animals. The first settlers may have been Peruvian Indians, and today there are about 6,200 people living on the islands.

LESSON 12

How Could New Species Develop?

After four billion years of natural selection, there are millions of different kinds of living organisms on the earth. You belong to one of about 23,000 species of land animals with backbones. But at one time none of these species existed. So where did the first land animals with backbones come from?

Four hundred million years ago, the oceans began to shrink. Competition among sea creatures with backbones became fierce. Adaptations, traits that let organisms compete successfully in an environment, allowed some of these animals to move around on dry land. These early amphibians soon grew strong and reproduced. Insects had made the move to land several million years before, so the amphibians had plenty to eat when they arrived.

Early amphibians stayed near riverbanks and beaches. But later, some species developed dry, scaly skin and began to lay hard-shelled eggs. These adaptations let them live and breed far from water—and far from amphibians that ate other amphibians.

46 SUBCONCEPT THREE: HOW NEW SPECIES DEVELOP

SCIENCE LITERACY:
Recognize patterns and relationships.

Have students read page 46. Help them to understand that the sea creatures with backbones that became amphibians didn't choose to grow legs and develop lungs. Rather, the sea animals that acquired those features by chance had an advantage in a world of shrinking seas. Thus natural selection ensured that the sea animals survived on dry land and passed their traits along to their offspring.

After students have read the entire section, ask:
Do you think the development of amphibians, reptiles, and mammals took place gradually or all at once? *(Scientists once thought natural selection worked gradually over millions of years. Now they theorize that new species may appear relatively suddenly in geological time—but that still means a huge number of years in human terms.)*

Be sure students understand that the principles of natural selection apply to plants as well as animals. As an example, you might cite the numerous instances in which flowers have evolved shapes or colors that attract pollinating insects.

Help students to see that warm-blooded animals can live in a much wider range of environments than cold-blooded animals. This exposure to many different environments offers more opportunities for survival and can lead to the formation of more new species.

Reptiles ruled the land, sea, and air for almost 235 million years. Early reptiles were the ancestors of mammals, dinosaurs, crocodiles, turtles, snakes, and lizards. The extinction of the dinosaurs allowed the mammals to take over. In the same way, the extinction of flying reptiles gave birds an extra opportunity.

The body temperature of cold-blooded amphibians and reptiles changes with their surroundings. Warm-blooded mammals keep the same temperature wherever they are. How do you think this adaptation helped new mammal species develop?

▼ These fish, amphibians, reptiles, dinosaurs, and mammals belong to different geological periods. By picturing them together in one scene, the pattern of change over time becomes clearer.

Information Connection:
Using reference books

Have students read the first paragraph and locate the Galápagos Islands on a map. Ask: **What type of climate would you expect to find on the Galápagos Islands?** *(Students will see from the map that the islands are near the equator, so the climate is warm.)* **How do you think the location of the Galápagos affected the way the finches developed there?** *(The isolation of these islands made it difficult, though not impossible, for birds from the mainland to get there. The few that made it had little competition from other birds at first. The species that developed there may have been unable to fly to or survive on the mainland.)*

Ask students to read the remainder of the selection and examine the drawings. After looking at the drawings, students will probably notice the different shapes and sizes of the finches' beaks. The *Beagle* voyage enabled Darwin to collect specimens and to document actual observations. This provided him with the information he needed to back up his ideas on natural selection.

In *Charles Darwin and Evolution*, students will find out more about the evolution of the Galápagos finches. **What other species varied from island to island?** *(mockingbirds, tortoises, and flowers)*

Do you think samples of specimens, drawings, or charts, and photographs are always necessary for scientific research? *(Students will probably realize that visual aids and specimen samplings are important because they help to verify specific observations.)*

This is a good time to distribute ThinkMat 12.

12 How Could New Species Develop?

SIX OF DARWIN'S 13 SPECIES OF GALÁPAGOS FINCHES

▲ Small ground finch

▲ Small tree finch

▲ Large tree finch

▲ Large ground finch

▲ Warbler finch

▲ Cactus ground finch

Exploration Connection:
Using reference books

The idea that new species develop from older species has been around a long time. But Charles Darwin was the first person to state this idea as scientific theory. As a young naturalist sailing on the H.M.S. *Beagle* in the 1830s, his job was to study the wildlife wherever the ship landed. In the Galapagos Islands, about 970 km from Ecuador, he got his first clue about natural selection.

Although there were very few animals on the islands, Darwin counted 13 species of finches. These 13 species were found nowhere else in the world. What's the first thing you notice about the finches in the drawings at the top of the page? Each species, Darwin observed, was well suited to the Galápagos and to what it ate there. He concluded that the 13 species of Galápagos finches were descendants of a single species from South America.

How important was the voyage of the *Beagle* to Darwin's thinking about natural selection? Turn to pages 8–14 in *Charles Darwin and Evolution*.

48 SUBCONCEPT THREE: HOW NEW SPECIES DEVELOP

Student Pages 48–49

Closer to Home: How one mammal went back

Ask students: **What might happen if all members of a population were identical genetically?** *(If there were a major change in the population's environment, none might survive. Genetic variation gives a species flexibility so that at least some of its members may survive in a changed environment.)*

- Over time, ancestors of the whale became adapted to a water environment. They succeeded at surviving and reproducing in the water where there was less competition.

Diverse perspectives

At one time whales were frequently hunted for their baleen and blubber. People made corsets, fishing rods, and whips from baleen, and oil was made from blubber.

Rock carvings about 4,000 years old show that Norwegians may have been the first to hunt whales in the sea. In the 900s the Basque people of northern Spain and southern France began the earliest whaling industry. Native Americans hunted whales from shore, while colonial Americans sent out expeditions. Modern technology greatly increased the efficiency of whaling. Eventually this threatened the survival of several species. As a result, in 1982 and 1991 the International Whaling Commission voted for moratoriums on commercial whaling.

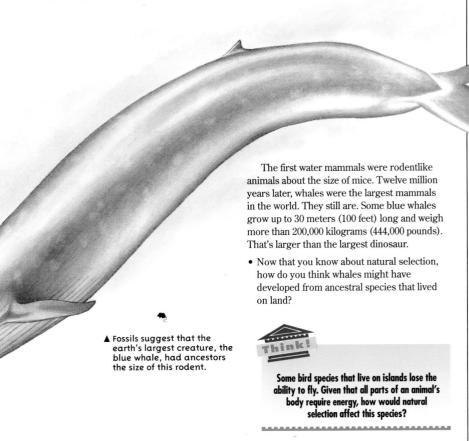

Closer to Home:
How one mammal went back

Many people are surprised to find out that whales are not fish. But did you know that their oldest-known ancestors were land animals? Like other land animals with backbones, the whale's ancestors developed from creatures that came from the sea. But unlike most land animals, their ancestors returned to the sea—about 50 million years ago, during the Tertiary Period.

No one knows why the whale's ancestors went back to water, although there are several theories to explain the return. Some people think the whale's ancestors left land because the competition for food and territory was getting too fierce. In the age of mammals, the ocean became yet another territory for mammals to explore.

The first water mammals were rodentlike animals about the size of mice. Twelve million years later, whales were the largest mammals in the world. They still are. Some blue whales grow up to 30 meters (100 feet) long and weigh more than 200,000 kilograms (444,000 pounds). That's larger than the largest dinosaur.

- Now that you know about natural selection, how do you think whales might have developed from ancestral species that lived on land?

▲ Fossils suggest that the earth's largest creature, the blue whale, had ancestors the size of this rodent.

Think!

Some bird species that live on islands lose the ability to fly. Given that all parts of an animal's body require energy, how would natural selection affect this species?

Think!

Ask students to think about an island environment. If there are no predators and plenty of food on the island, the birds wouldn't need to fly. The bird wouldn't need to eat as much food to survive as it would if it had wing tissue to maintain.

LESSON THINKING SKILLS:
Recognizing Cause and Effect;
Recognizing Patterns and Relationships

49

Assessment Options

Using Students' Process Performance and Recorded Observations

Written Options

1. Students' responses on their ThinkMat should give you a clear idea of their understanding of the lesson concept. Use Student Benchmarks to analyze their answers.

2. In addition, ask students to write a paragraph about adaptations that would be advantageous in their environment.

Student Benchmarks

Proficient: Students discuss how some characteristics allow organisms to survive in changing environments and that organisms with those characteristics will reproduce.

Apprentice: Students discuss how a new species could develop as a result of adaptation to environmental changes.

Novice: Students discuss how environmental changes play a key role in how a new species might develop but may not understand the role of adaptation.

Portfolio

Students may decide they want to include the ThinkMat from this lesson in their Portfolio. In addition, they may want to include the Written Options from above.

Oral Options

Here are some ideas for class discussion of this content lesson. Student Benchmarks will give you an idea of how well students understand the lesson concept.

1. Ask students questions about how certain adaptations might have evolved over time. For example, do you think the early amphibians could walk quickly or did they probably crawl?

2. How students answer the Think question will also give you a good idea of their understanding of the lesson concept.

The following questions can also be used to assess understanding of the lesson concept:

3. What adaptations do you think humans might develop a million years from now? *(Accept any reasonable answer. Students might suggest a less muscular body, larger eyes, filters in their lungs, and so forth.)*

4. Suppose a species of animal called amps has lived successfully on an island that has no predators. One day several predators (chomps) happen to swim to the island. Describe what may take place and why. *(Students may suggest that because the amps didn't develop the defense mechanisms they need to survive an invasion of predators, they'd be wiped out. The chomps might also die out when their food source is gone, or they might return to the mainland.)*

Reteaching the Novice

To be sure students understand how adaptations could lead to the development of new species, ask them to describe the different types of physical features in an ocean environment and one on land near water. Once students have compared both environments, have them identify the kinds of adaptations that early amphibians developed to make the transition from water to land. Emphasize that adaptations usually take place over time and correspond to changes in the environment. Do you think all adaptations develop into new species?

Integrating Your Curriculum

CONNECTING TO LIFE SCIENCE

The Galápagos

Divide the class into 13 groups and assign a different island of the Galápagos to each group. Let students research their island, finding out what animals and plants live there. Have students draw pictures and captions of their animals and plants. Make sure they also describe the environment and climate. Then line up all the pictures on the wall or chalkboard and have the class compare the islands.

INTEGRATING ART

Illustrating Species Richness

Species richness is the variety of living things in an environment. Some environments are more species-rich than others. For example, deserts have a low species density compared to tropical forests. The richness increases with habitat complexity and the size of an area. A greater variety of species will develop to inhabit the greater variety of habitats in a larger and more complex environment. Smaller areas support smaller populations, which are more prone to extinction. Species richness is also greater in areas near the equator, possibly because the more hospitable weather enables species to survive long enough to carve specific niches for themselves. Invite groups of students to create a display that shows the comparative variety of species in different environments such as oceans, shores, wetlands, deserts, grasslands, tundras, and forests. They can draw or cut out pictures of plant and animal species from each environment. They can also collect and present facts on cards about the range and number of species in each environment.

INTEGRATING GEOGRAPHY AND LANGUAGE ARTS

Follow the Beagle

Homework Option

The *Beagle* was one of several British sailing vessels used by scientists to collect biological and geological samples. Provide students with a map showing the route traveled by the *Beagle* (see map in *Charles Darwin and Evolution*, page 8). Have them use a globe or atlas to identify and label the islands and countries the *Beagle* traveled to. Then have them choose a location and find out about some of the present-day cultures as well as plants and animals that populate that area. Encourage students to write a few paragraphs about their findings.

CURIOSITY PLACE

Some scientists believe that whales evolved from small, rodentlike mammals.

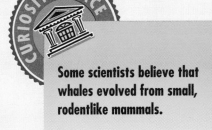

How Are Species Related to Each Other?

Student Pages 50–53

Lesson Road Map

In the last lesson: Students investigated ways in which new species may develop.

In this lesson: Students explore the structural similarities between living species. In Part One they observe living organisms with similar structures. In Part Two they compare skeletons.

In the next lesson: Students will think about the effects environmental changes have on living species and will communicate how evolution is a continual process.

The Story Line

Grade Level Concept
Different species have inhabited the earth at different times.

Subconcepts
Fossils provide evidence that many species that once inhabited the earth have become extinct.

Changes in the environment or human intervention can result in changes in the characteristics of a population, which are passed on to succeeding generations.

Variation and natural selection have resulted in the evolution of new species.

Lesson Concept
Structural similarities are evidence that living species share common ancestors.

Getting Organized

This lesson requires two 50-minute sessions.

Materials per Group:
4 28-g (1-oz) sticks (each a different color) of nondrying modeling clay

PART ONE

Advance Preparation:
Gather materials. Divide each 4-oz bar of clay into quarters.

Materials per Group:
ThinkMat 13
28-g (1-oz) modeling clay (any color)
Tape
Toothpicks

PART TWO

Advance Preparation:
Gather materials.

ALSO FOR THIS LESSON:

ThinkMat 13
For use with the Exploration

LabMats 13A and 13B
Recording sheets for the Explorations

For Science Browsers
"Fossil Whale Feet" Student page 68

Content Background

H istory," writes natural historian Stephen Jay Gould, "cannot be reproduced in a flask." Unlike other sciences, natural history relies more on observation and deduction than on experimentation. In trying to find out if species are related to one another, scientists look for clues in the fossil record as well as in the structures of living organisms.

Charles Darwin believed that as a species evolves over time, organisms will be marked by unexplained physical peculiarities carried over from the past. There are a number of examples that support Darwin's idea. For instance, human fetuses have tails that become less apparent as they mature. The coccyx at the base of the spine is the vestige of this embryonic tail.

Structural similarities between two organisms can indicate that they have common ancestry. What constitutes similarity, however, is a tricky question. Certain animals may have forelimbs with similar structure, but with very different functions for them. In such cases, the forelimbs were probably inherited from a common ancestor but adapted to different tasks in different species. On the other hand, even though the wings of birds, bats, and butterflies are similar, they weren't inherited from the same predecessor. Usually structure rather than function is the key, and the closer the similarities between structures, the more likely it is that the organisms sharing these structures are related.

Teachers' Bookshelf

Stein, Sara. *The Evolution Book.* New York: Workman, 1986.

Johanson, Donald E. *Lucy: The Beginning of Humankind.* New York: Simon and Schuster, 1990.

Theme Connection: Patterns of Change

T he structure of given species provides a clue to its evolutionary history. Similarly, Earth's history can be revealed by examining its landforms.

Considering Second-Language Learners

U se the opening paragraph of the lesson to help students understand and get practice on the use of the present perfect tense. After reading it aloud, write the following sentence on the chalkboard: *I've visited a zoo _____.* Then ask: "Have you visited a zoo?" Have students complete the sentence based on their own experiences. (For example: "I've visited a zoo many times." "I've visited a zoo only one time.") If someone has never visited a zoo, read aloud the correct sentence order and write it on the chalkboard: *I've never visited a zoo.* Continue by asking students to describe the animals they've seen. Ask them if there were any similarities between species. Encourage students to describe the similar physical characteristics.

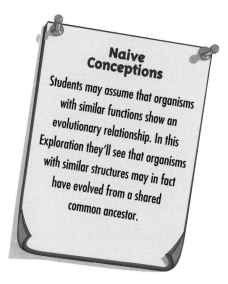

Naive Conceptions

Students may assume that organisms with similar functions show an evolutionary relationship. In this Exploration they'll see that organisms with similar structures may in fact have evolved from a shared common ancestor.

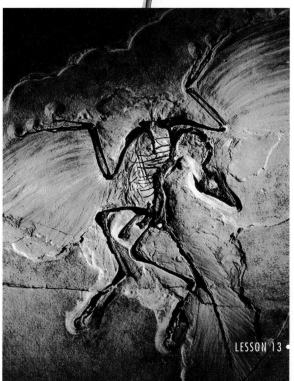

LESSON 13 | **Part One**

What do we know?
What do we want to know?

1

ACTIVATE

EXPLORATION:
Make models of forelimbs.

Materials per Group: 4 28-g (1-oz) sticks (each a different color) of nondrying modeling clay

Suggested Grouping: four

Approximate Time: 30 minutes

Classroom Management: Copy LabMat 13A. Since the first Exploration is necessary for a clear understanding of the second Exploration, you won't be able to jigsaw this lesson.

Process Skills and Objectives
Students will:

- **observe** similarities in the forelimbs of certain animals

- **compare** the functions of similarly constructed forelimbs

- **communicate** that there are many similarities among different species

Opening the Discussion
Have students read the introductory paragraph on page 50. Ask: **What pets do you have at home? What animals do you have in your neighborhood? What animals do you see in zoos?** Work with students to make a class list.

Are any of these animals similar? *(Have students group the animals according to any physical characteristics they choose, such as size, coloring, specific features [wings, tails, eyes, and so on].)* Write the categories and answers on the Recording Board.

LESSON 13

How Are Species Related to Each Other?

If you've visited a zoo or an aquarium, you know there are many differences between living things. But have you noticed how many similarities there are? Take a close second look at the animals you've seen in this book so far. What characteristics do they have in common?

Exploration:
Make models of forelimbs.

You need:
Modeling clay (4 colors)

❶ Compare the drawings of the four forelimbs on the next page.

❷ Count the bones in each forelimb. Record the data.

❸ Make a model of the crocodile forelimb. Use a different color of clay for the bones in each part—upper limb, lower limb, wrist, and hand.

❹ Now change the model of the crocodile forelimb into one of the other forelimbs. You can add or subtract clay to change the size and shape of the bones.

Interpret your results.

- How did you change the clay model from one forelimb to another? Did you make a lot of changes or only a few?

- How is a chimpanzee's arm like a crocodile's leg, a bird's wing, or a whale's flipper?

- Living organisms with similar structures often have a common ancestor. Based on your observations, would you say the common ancestor of these animals used its forelimbs to move itself or to pick things up?

EXPLORATION:
Make models of forelimbs.

Troubleshooting: Students shouldn't worry about their skill as sculptors. The important thing is to approximate the size, shape, and relationship of the bones.

2 After distributing LabMat 13A, ask students: **Which animal has the most bones in its forelimb? Which has the fewest?** *(All the animals have one bone in the upper forelimb and two in the lower forelimb. They differ in*

the number of bones they have in the wrists, hands, and fingers.) Have students list other differences.

3 4 You might want to have each group member work on a different part of the forelimb. Make sure students know that they're to make one model and then alter it rather than making separate models of each forelimb.

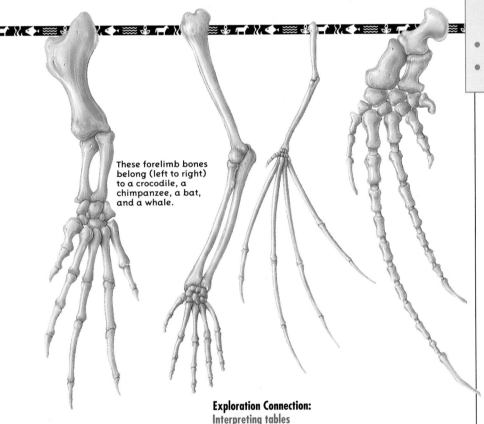

These forelimb bones belong (left to right) to a crocodile, a chimpanzee, a bat, and a whale.

Exploration Connection:
Interpreting tables

How do people keep track of all the similarities between organisms? For as long as people have studied living things, they have grouped them based on their similarities and differences. Many plants and animals are still grouped according to a system invented by an eighteenth-century Swedish naturalist named Carolus Linnaeus.

Look at the table. It shows how two organisms are classified using the system Linnaeus invented. What similarities do you notice?

LINNAEUS'S GROUPS	Subdivisions for RED FOX	Subdivisions for HUMAN
Kingdom	Animalia	Animalia
Phylum	Chordata	Chordata
Sub-phylum	Vertebrata	Vertebrata
Class	Mammalia	Mammalia
Order	Carnivora	Primate
Family	Canidae	Hominidae
Genus	*Vulpes*	*Homo*
Species	*Vulpes fulva*	*Homo sapiens*

Interpret Your Results

- Students will probably say that only a few changes were needed, such as changing the lengths and thicknesses.
- They are structurally very similar.
- The common ancestor used its forelimbs to move.

Exploration Connection:
Interpreting tables

After examining the table, students will see that red foxes and humans share some of the same subdivisions: *Animalia, Chordata, Vertebrata,* and *Mammalia.*

Ask students: **Why do you think scientists use tables to record their data?** *(Students will probably realize that a table can be used to organize numerous data. It is also easier to refer to a table.)* You may want to have students add another species to the table.

51

EXPLORATION:
Compare old and new skeletons.

❹ Make sure students know they are to choose only one feature of the dinosaur and bird for their models.

❺ Have students think about how some physical similarities may have enabled certain animals to survive in their environment.

Process Skills and Objectives
Students will:

• **observe** the structures of animals

• **compare** the structure of one animal to that of another to see if they share the same ancestor

PREPARING FOR THE EXPLORATION

Materials per Group: ThinkMat 13, 28-g (1-oz) modeling clay (any color), tape, toothpicks

Suggested Grouping: pairs

Approximate Time: 25 minutes

Classroom Management: Copy LabMat 13B and ThinkMat 13. For students who finish the Exploration quickly, have them do one of the Options on page 107.

EXPLORATION:
Compare old and new skeletons.

❶❷ Ask students: **Does the archaeopteryx remind you of an animal other than the dinosaur or the bird?** (*Accept any reasonable answer that shows students recognize structural similarities.*) Distribute LabMat 13B.

❸ Have students think about the dimensions of the bones—length, thickness, width.

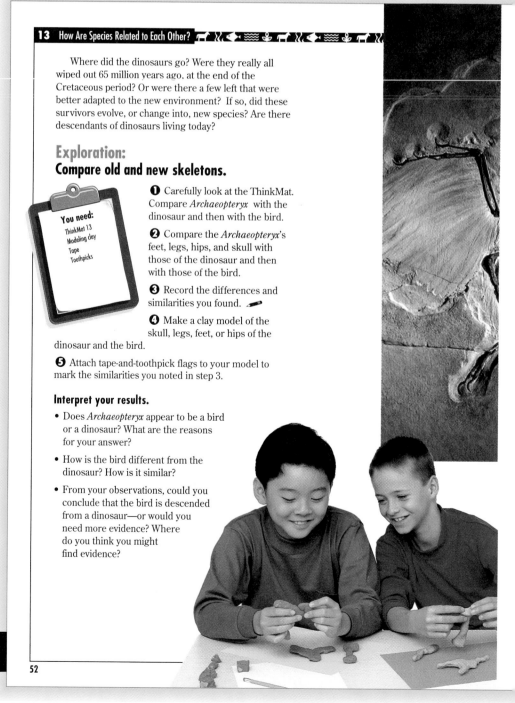

13 How Are Species Related to Each Other?

Where did the dinosaurs go? Were they really all wiped out 65 million years ago, at the end of the Cretaceous period? Or were there a few left that were better adapted to the new environment? If so, did these survivors evolve, or change into, new species? Are there descendants of dinosaurs living today?

Exploration:
Compare old and new skeletons.

You need:
ThinkMat 13
Modeling clay
Tape
Toothpicks

❶ Carefully look at the ThinkMat. Compare *Archaeopteryx* with the dinosaur and then with the bird.

❷ Compare the *Archaeopteryx*'s feet, legs, hips, and skull with those of the dinosaur and then with those of the bird.

❸ Record the differences and similarities you found.

❹ Make a clay model of the skull, legs, feet, or hips of the dinosaur and the bird.

❺ Attach tape-and-toothpick flags to your model to mark the similarities you noted in step 3.

Interpret your results.

• Does *Archaeopteryx* appear to be a bird or a dinosaur? What are the reasons for your answer?

• How is the bird different from the dinosaur? How is it similar?

• From your observations, could you conclude that the bird is descended from a dinosaur—or would you need more evidence? Where do you think you might find evidence?

52

Interpret Your Results

• It's difficult to decide because the archaeopteryx shares characteristics of both the bird and the dinosaur.

• The bird is different because it has feathers. The bird and the dinosaur have very similar skeletons.

• The bird might be descended from a dinosaur, but more information is needed. Scientists may find evidence in fossils.

Closer to Home: A tail from long ago

After students have read the section, ask: **Why do you think humans no longer have tailbones?** *(Students will probably say that tails were no longer needed for survival.)*

• Point out that hip bones create sockets for legs to fit into. The pelvis bones on a whale suggest that it may have evolved from an animal that once had legs and lived on land.

• Dolphins would have hip bones because they are mammals, and all mammals have similar bone structures.

This is a good time to distribute ThinkMat 13.

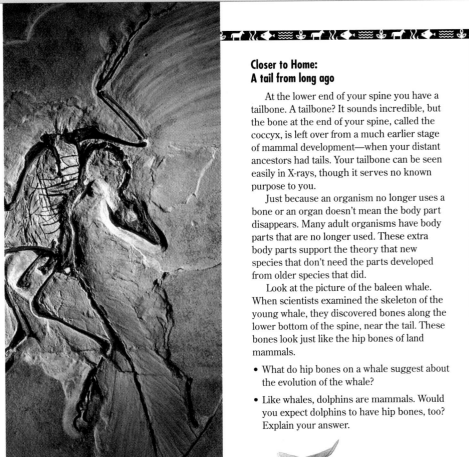

Closer to Home:
A tail from long ago

At the lower end of your spine you have a tailbone. A tailbone? It sounds incredible, but the bone at the end of your spine, called the coccyx, is left over from a much earlier stage of mammal development—when your distant ancestors had tails. Your tailbone can be seen easily in X-rays, though it serves no known purpose to you.

Just because an organism no longer uses a bone or an organ doesn't mean the body part disappears. Many adult organisms have body parts that are no longer used. These extra body parts support the theory that new species that don't need the parts developed from older species that did.

Look at the picture of the baleen whale. When scientists examined the skeleton of the young whale, they discovered bones along the lower bottom of the spine, near the tail. These bones look just like the hip bones of land mammals.

• What do hip bones on a whale suggest about the evolution of the whale?

• Like whales, dolphins are mammals. Would you expect dolphins to have hip bones, too? Explain your answer.

▲ A fossil of *Archaeopteryx* has traces of what covered its bones.

A vestigal organ resembling a land mammal's hip bones can be found near a baleen whale's tail.

Think!

You know some of the traits whales share with other mammals. What traits do they share with fish? How do you think whales got these traits?

Think!

Whales have tails, fins, and streamlined shapes similar to fish. All of these traits are adaptations to living in water. Some date from the period since the whale's return to water.

LESSON THINKING SKILLS:
Contrasting; Organizing Information; Drawing Conclusions

SUBCONCEPT THREE: HOW NEW SPECIES DEVELOP **53**

Assessment Options

Using Students' Process Performance and Recorded Observations

Written Options

1. Students' responses on their LabMats and ThinkMat should give you a clear idea of their understanding of the lesson concept. Use Student Benchmarks to analyze their answers.

2. In addition, have students make lists of the comparisons they made of the structures of the animals in both Explorations.

Student Benchmarks

Proficient: Students identify structural similarities in different species and infer their common ancestry.

Apprentice: Students discuss that different species may have come from a common ancestor. They'll see similarities in structure among species.

Novice: Students demonstrate how structural similarities connect certain species to the same ancestor.

Portfolio

Students may decide they want to include the LabMats from this lesson in their Portfolio. In addition, they may want to include an Option from page 107.

Oral Options

Listen to students as they do the Explorations. Student Benchmarks will give you an idea of how well they understand the lesson concept.

1. In Part One, ask students about the similarities and differences in the four different forelimbs. Do all the forelimbs move the same way? Are they alike in shape?

2. In Part Two, ask students if the archaeopteryx might be related to animals other than the dinosaur or bird. Explain that bone structure rather than function is the key to seeing if animals are related.

3. How students answer the Think question will also give you a good idea of their understanding of the lesson concept.

The following questions can also be used to assess understanding of the lesson concept:

4. Which kind of evidence would better support the claim that two species are related to a common ancestor—similarities in the structure of a body part or similarities in function? *(Similarities in structure provide better evidence because similarities in function can be the result of separate adaptations of several different species to the same environment.)*

5. Why doesn't a species get rid of unnecessary body parts immediately? *(Evolution works slowly and takes advantage of variations that occur.)*

Reteaching the Novice

Have students examine the models of a crocodile's forelimb they made in Exploration 1. Ask them to make a list of the type of movements that can be made with each part of the forelimb. What type of movements can be made with human forelimbs? Ask them to compare any similarities or differences.

Display the picture of the archaeopteryx and have students examine the models of dinosaurs they made in Exploration 2. Ask for volunteers to point to the physical characteristics that make the archaeopteryx similar to a dinosaur or bird.

Integrating Your Curriculum

CONNECTING TO LIFE SCIENCE

Structural Similarities in Plants

Provide (or have students gather) four different kinds of plants. Working in groups, have students use hand lenses to carefully examine the various parts of the plants.

Materials: 4 plants, hand lenses

Write descriptions and draw diagrams of the main structures of the plants that they observe.

List at least four similarities between the plants, and what function they think some of the common features might serve.

After groups have finished their descriptions, lead the class in a discussion on the similarities among the plants. Have students suggest the characteristics of a possible ancestor to the four plants.

CONNECTING TO LIFE SCIENCE

Be a Detective

Use the book *After Man: A Zoology of the Future* to help students think about the clues to an organism's ancestry that can be found in its physical structure. Select an animal from the book and provide students with copies of its description. Then offer students clues to help them guess what the organism evolved from. For example, tell them where the organism is found, what it eats, what its habitat is like, what its predators and prey are, and so on. Use descriptions provided in the book so students can narrow down their answers to a close guess. When you reveal (or when students guess) the answer, lead students in a discussion about structural similarities between the ancestors of the animal and the fictional future animal.

INTEGRATING REFERENCE SOURCES

Make Your Own Encyclopedia

Homework Option

Have students choose a species whose evolutionary history is fairly complete, such as the horse. (Students may choose a longer time span, as long as the general evolutionary path can be traced.) Have them make a book with several sheets of 8 1/2" x 11" paper folded and stapled together. On the inside cover, have them draw the family tree of the species or another diagram of its evolution with dates. Then have them devote a page to each stage of evolutionary development they find in their research. Ask students to draw each organism and write a brief statement about it.

CURIOSITY PLACE

Researchers have found a series of fossils illustrating the evolution of today's horse from a dog-sized mammal, genus *Hyracotherium*, which walked on tiptoe and lived in forests 55 million years ago.

Are Species Changing Today?

Student Pages 54–57

Lesson Road Map

In the last lesson: Students explored the structural similarities between living species.

In this lesson: Students think about the effects environmental changes have on living species and communicate how evolution is a continual process.

In the next lesson: Students will identify the problems they might encounter when designing a community of organisms that might evolve in 1 million years.

The Story Line

Grade Level Concept
Different species have inhabited the earth at different times.

Subconcepts
Fossils provide evidence that many species that once inhabited the earth have become extinct.

Changes in the environment or human intervention can result in changes in the characteristics of a population, which are passed on to succeeding generations.

Variation and natural selection have resulted in the evolution of new species.

Lesson Concept
Evolution is an ongoing process that continues to occur today.

Getting Organized

This lesson requires one 40-minute session.

Materials per Group:
ThinkMat 14

Advance Preparation:
Gather materials.

ALSO FOR THIS LESSON:

ThinkMat 14

Reviewing the subconcept and for use with the Exploration

LabMat 14

Recording sheet for the Exploration

Content Background

A species doesn't consciously "choose" to adapt; nor does the process of evolution move along a set path toward a goal. Although the ancestors of living animals often look strange to us, they were as well adapted to their environments as present-day organisms are.

Evolutionary change results mainly from interactions between organisms and their environments. As environments change, certain traits become more favorable. Organisms with these traits survive, reproduce, and pass on these traits—or adaptations— to their offspring. Adaptations can take the form of physical and structural traits, such as the shape of a bird's beak, or behavioral traits, such as the mating dances of certain birds.

Humans may intervene in this natural process, as students will learn when they read about the attempt to breed African bees and European bees. In these cases of artificial selection, humans select certain traits that they consider desirable, such as the ability to gather more nectar, and try to breed more organisms with these traits.

Vocabulary

evolution: The scientific theory that groups of organisms change their shape and structure over long periods of time.

Teachers' Bookshelf

Shella, Ellen Ruppel. "Waves of Creation." *Discover.* May 1993, pp. 54—62.

Whitfield, Philip. *From So Simple a Beginning?* New York: Macmillan, 1993.

Theme Connection: Patterns of Change

Evolution is an ongoing process that results in organisms that are well suited to their environments. Similarly, people are constantly inventing and changing technology to suit human needs.

Considering Second-Language Learners

The lesson title provides a good example of how the gerund is used to form the present continuous: "Are Species Changing Today?" Invite students to play an oral transformation game, changing "species" to specific animals, using both singular and plural nouns ("Is the dinosaur living today?"). You could also focus on the gerund as an adjective. Write on the chalkboard: "Things that live are called living things." Circle the *-ing* ending and explain that *living things* means "things that live." Then ask questions such as: "What would you call things that grow?" *(growing things)* "What would you call animals that crawl?" *(crawling animals)*, and so on.

Naive Conceptions

Students may think that evolution is something that happened only in the past. This lesson shows that evolution is an ongoing process.

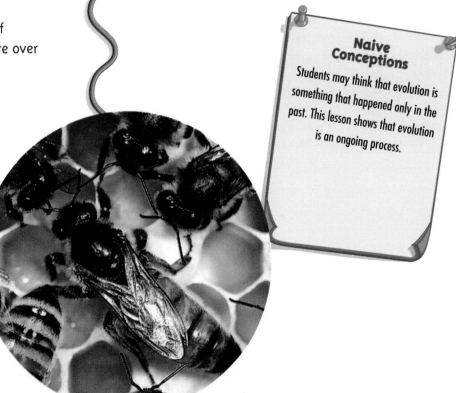

LESSON 14

What do we know?
What do we want to know?

1
ACTIVATE

EXPLORATION:
Design the animals of the future.

Process Skills and Objectives

Students will:

- **predict** how changes in an environment affect the evolution of new species

- **compare** the obvious adaptations of other species

Opening the Discussion

Have students read the first paragraph on page 54. Based on what they've learned in previous lessons, ask: **Why do some species become extinct while others survive?** *(Students will probably recall that some members of a species will develop adaptations that enable them to survive in a changing environment, while others won't.)*

Do you think Earth's environment is still changing? How? *(Students may mention natural disasters, changes in landforms and climate, and pollution as sources of environmental change.)* Write students' responses on the Recording Board.

PREPARING FOR THE EXPLORATION

Materials per Group: ThinkMat 14

Suggested Grouping: pairs

Approximate Time: 20 minutes

Classroom Management: Copy LabMat 14 and ThinkMat 14. For students who finish before others, have them do one of the Options on page 115.

LESSON 14

Are Species Changing Today?

In the 3.5 billion years that living things have inhabited the earth, many species have become extinct and many others have evolved, or developed, into new species. But what about today? You know that species have become extinct in your lifetime. But have we reached the end of <u>evolution</u>, the process in which living things developed over time, or are animals, plants, and other organisms still evolving?

Exploration:
Design the animals of the future.

You need:
ThinkMat 14

❶ The earth's environments have changed since dinosaurs roamed the land. Look carefully at the wetland habitat on your ThinkMat. On your LabMat, draw the same scene in a hot, dry future.

❷ Choose two small wetland inhabitants— a duck and a turtle, or a dragonfly and a water rat— and imagine they have each evolved into a species that can survive in the new environment. Describe each new species, and add the animals to your drawing.

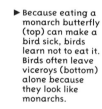

▶ Because eating a monarch butterfly (top) can make a bird sick, birds learn not to eat it. Birds often leave viceroys (bottom) alone because they look like monarchs.

Interpret your results.

- What does your wetland of the future look like? Why do you think it might look this way?

- How have your wetland animals evolved in this changed environment? What body parts help them survive? These changed body parts are adaptations.

▶ Run your eyes along this picture quickly, from left to right. You'll see how the sudden flight of a herd of zebras can confuse a hungry lion right out of a meal.

54 SUBCONCEPT THREE: HOW NEW SPECIES DEVELOP

Student Pages 54–55

EXPLORATION:
Design the animals of the future.

◎ **Troubleshooting:** To help students think of ways their animals might have adapted to a hotter, drier climate, suggest that they consider present-day desert animals. What characteristics allow them to survive?

❶ Remind students to include plant life in their drawings. Distribute LabMat 14.

❷ Suggest that students consider vegetation, temperature, rainfall, and the lay of the land when imagining their animals. Make sure students choose animals whose present-day natural habitats aren't hot, dry areas such as deserts.

Interpret Your Results

- There might be fewer plants, fewer trees, and not much grass. Students might predict that the land has changed through erosion.

- Students may imagine tough, leathery skin to help the animals maintain moisture.

Exploration Connection:
Using reference books

You know what adaptations are. But which ones do you recognize? Some adaptations are easy to spot. Animal colorings that provide camouflage are adaptations that have evolved over millions of years.

Some adaptations are less obvious. The stripes on a zebra would seem to make the black-and-white animal an easy target for a lion. But when zebras run in a herd, their moving stripes make it hard for the lion to focus on an individual zebra.

Make a list of the animals pictured in *Charles Darwin and Evolution*. Explain how you think each animal uses its body covering to compete more successfully.

Exploration Connection:
Using reference books

After skimming through *Charles Darwin and Evolution* students might suggest in their animal list that a marine iguana's scaly earth-colored skin (page 14) helps it to blend in with the rocks. The stag's antlers (page 24) enable it to defend itself.

Have students look at the illustrations on pages 22–23. Ask: **Judging from the group of elephants pictured, what features might have evolved to adapt to the environment?** *(Students may suggest features such as longer ears, different-shaped tusks, and long and narrow trunks.)*

This is a good time to distribute ThinkMat 14.

Closer to Home: New bee on the block

After reading the section, ask students: **How can beekeepers create gentler bees?** (Using artificial selection, beekeepers can select the gentlest bees in each generation and use them to breed new generations of gentler bees.)

Judging from the map on page 57, why do you think researchers might have thought the African honeybees would adapt well to South America? (Since both regions are subtropical, researchers probably thought the honeybees would adapt well.)

• They might be less aggressive because there would probably be fewer predators in the environment.

---

14 Are Species Changing Today?

▲ Bees live in colonies. The one queen bee in a bee colony is the mother of all the other bees.

▲ Most of the bees in a colony are female workers.

Closer to Home: New bee on the block

Sometimes evolution gets a helping hand from humans. The results can be a big problem.

Honeybees are social insects that live in large colonies of 50,000 or more. People have raised honeybees and gathered honey for thousands of years. Honey was part of the human diet long before sugar cane was grown. Because there were no native honeybees in the Americas, Europeans brought their own bees when they colonized the continent hundreds of years ago. The honeybee has thrived in many different environments, and people all over the world today use modern methods to raise these insects.

In 1956, a researcher in Brazil decided to import some honeybees from Africa. He knew the African bees were good nectar gatherers, and he hoped they would breed with his European bees and produce more honey. However, something happened that he didn't foresee. The new bees—the offspring of the European bees and the African bees—were much harder to work with.

▲ A beekeeper in protective clothing works on a hive. The hive is designed to make it easy for the beekeeper to remove honey.

Student Pages 56–57

56 SUBCONCEPT THREE: HOW NEW SPECIES DEVELOP

Diverse perspectives

You know that natural changes in the environment are the forces that make species adapt or disappear. But changes in the environment caused by human actions also threaten and/or alter many plant and animal species. People can also threaten the way of life for other human societies. All around the world, indigenous or aboriginal people—the first people to inhabit the areas where they live—face what has been termed "cultural extinction."

For example, today, groups of native people in Brazil, such as the Yanomami Indians, depend on the rain forest for their survival. If and when the rain forest is destroyed, they'll be displaced and may have to adapt to a new environment and culture. Some organizations, like the World Council of Indigenous Peoples, help groups keep their land and livelihood. They also help them find ways to adapt to changes. These organizations say that the rest of the world may have something to learn from native people. Many indigenous people, after all, have learned to live in harmony with the natural world.

▲ Male bees are called drones. Their job is to mate with the queen.

African honeybees come from an environment where they have many natural enemies. They are larger than most European bees, and when they are alarmed they attack in great numbers. The new breed of bees turned out to have the same defensive behavior.

Since 1956, the new bees have spread. As they spread, they breed with local bees. Beekeepers in all of these areas must learn to work with the new bees.

• Honeybees have fewer natural predators in the Americas than they have in Africa. How do you think the American descendants of the African honeybee may change in the far future? Explain your answer.

This would be a good opportunity to have students get on-line to share data and ideas about any type of displacement they know about in their area.

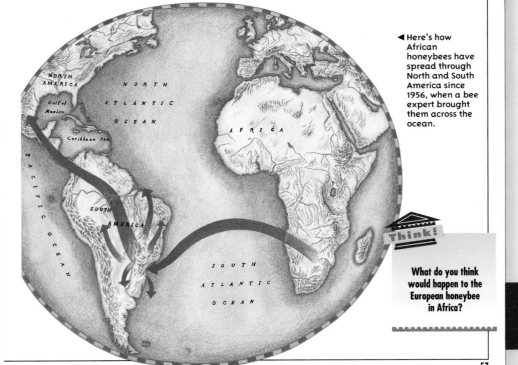

◄ Here's how African honeybees have spread through North and South America since 1956, when a bee expert brought them across the ocean.

Think!

What do you think would happen to the European honeybee in Africa?

Think!

It would probably get wiped out by the predators that have helped to form the African honeybee's defensive behavior.

LESSON THINKING SKILLS:
Recognizing Cause and Effect; Visualizing

57

Assessment Options

Using Students' Process Performance and Recorded Observations

Written Options

1. Students' responses on their LabMat and ThinkMat should give you a clear idea of their understanding of the lesson concept. Use Student Benchmarks to analyze their answers.

2. In addition, have students write captions for their drawings. Encourage them to use callouts (pointers) to point to the animals or plants that they're describing.

Oral Options

Listen to students as they do the Exploration. Student Benchmarks will give you an idea of how well they understand the lesson concept.

1. Ask students to imagine the phases in which the environment might have changed from a wetland habitat to a hot, dry landscape. Have them describe how animals and plants might have evolved through each phase.

2. How students answer the Think question will also give you a good idea of their understanding of the lesson concept.

The following questions can also be used to assess understanding of the lesson concept:

3. If the climate in the North and South poles became much warmer, what types of adaptations do you think polar bears might develop? *(Students may suggest that polar bears might need less hair and body fat.)*

4. What types of adaptations do you think arose during the evolution of certain types of wild cats into domestic cats? *(Students may suggest both physical and behavioral changes, such as smaller bodies and less defensive reactions toward humans.)*

Student Benchmarks

Proficient: Students discuss how some species may evolve in the future and are able to give examples of natural selection.

Apprentice: Students demonstrate that certain adaptations are well suited for specific environments.

Novice: Students demonstrate that as the environment continually changes, so do the species that live in that environment. They may not have a clear idea about what these adaptations are.

Portfolio

Students may decide they want to include the LabMat from this lesson in their Portfolio. In addition, they may want to include one of the Options from page 115.

Reteaching the Novice

Display the drawings that students made of the future in a hot and dry environment. Review why students selected certain species as predator and prey, and have them explain how those animals evolved. For example, some physical differences may be dry, tough skin and change of skin color to blend in with the landscape.

Then ask students to imagine that the area changed over time into a cold, arctic environment. How would those same animals evolve? Remind students to think of the gradual changes that might have lead up to the major change.

Integrating Your Curriculum

CONNECTING TO LIFE SCIENCE

Zebra Stripes

CHALLENGE · CHALLENGE

Have students work in pairs to test how a zebra's stripes can confuse other animals.

Materials: 3 sheets of blank white paper, scissors, black marker, paste

Fold the two sheets of blank paper in half lengthwise. Fold in half the other way, and in half again.

Cut along the folds so that there are eight rectangles.

Draw thick stripes on the rectangles with black markers.

Paste all the rectangles—some overlapping and at different angles—onto the third sheet of paper.

Now have the first student hold up the paper and pass it quickly in front of the second student's eyes. The second student should try to stay focused on the paper while it moves.

INTEGRATING ART

Disaster

About 240 million years ago in the Permian period of the Paleozoic era, a natural disaster wiped out 96 percent of all the living things on Earth. All the species that we know today evolved from the 4 percent that were left. Have students imagine how other natural disasters might wipe out all but one segment of the animal kingdom. Assign each group of students a different animal group (mammals, reptiles, amphibians, fish, insects). Then have students imagine and draw animals that might evolve from their animal group. Responses will vary, and students may be as imaginative as they like, but their responses should demonstrate an understanding of the mechanisms of natural selection. Their animals should have traits based on the traits of the ancestral animals assigned to their group.

INTEGRATING MATH AND GEOGRAPHY

World Population

Homework Option

The world's population has grown considerably during the twentieth century. By researching the population growth on each continent for this century, students will be able to see for themselves how the human species has increased in number. Have students find population figures on each continent for each decade of this century. Once they've gathered all the statistics, ask them to create a bar or line graph for the information. Are there increases for every continent? Compare the differences and similarities among continents. For each decade, ask students if they can explain the reason for the increase or decrease of the population on that continent. Remind them to consider such factors as wars, dramatic climatic changes, technological advances, economic changes, and migration between continents.

CURIOSITY PLACE

About 99 percent of all species that have ever lived are now extinct.

Lessons 15, 16, 17

Student Pages 58–63

Think Tank Road Map

In Lesson 15: Students will identify the problems they might encounter when designing a community of organisms that might evolve in 1 million years.

In Lesson 16: Students will identify some possible solutions to these problems by studying the evolution of the horse.

In Lesson 17: Students will put it all together as they design and make a model of a community of organisms that might be living on the earth 1 million years in the future.

The Story Line

Grade Level Concept
Different species have inhabited the earth at different times.

Subconcepts
Fossils provide evidence that many species that once inhabited the earth have become extinct.

Changes in the environment or human intervention can result in changes in the characteristics of a population, which are passed on to succeeding generations.

Variation and natural selection have resulted in the evolution of new species.

Think Tank Concept
Students make a model of a community of organisms that might evolve in 1 million years.

Getting Organized

The Think Tank requires three 45-minute sessions.

Materials per Group:
Paper
Pencils

Materials per Group:
Paper
Pencils

Materials per Group:
Clay
Cardboard
Sticks
Toothpicks
String
Pipe cleaners
Glue

LESSON 15

Advance Preparation:
Collect or have students bring in pictures illustrating the evolutionary stages of some common animals such as horses, dogs, and cats.

LESSON 16

Advance Preparation:
Gather materials.

LESSON 17

Advance Preparation:
You'll need a variety of materials for students who want to make 3-dimensional models. Provide computers and graphics programs for students interested in designing their models on the computer.

ALSO FOR THESE LESSONS:

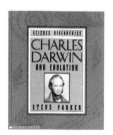

ThinkMats 15, 16, and 17

Thinking activities for the Think Tank

Think Tank Overview

Science fiction is more likely to deal with advances in human technology or life on faraway worlds than it is with the evolutionary changes of the earth's creatures. Yet for scientists, predicting the development of species should be an integral part of any construct of our planet's future. As student teams participate in the Think Tank project, they'll be coupling their powers of visualization with what they've learned about genetic variation, adaptation, interdependence of species, and natural selection to redesign a present-day community of organisms for survival 1 million years in the future.

The next three lessons provide a strategy for student teams to use as they face the challenge of redesigning and building a model of their chosen organism. In Lesson 15 they'll be introduced to the task and will identify the problems involved in redesigning an animal or plant to survive in 1 million years. After they've identified these problems, they'll brainstorm possible solutions. They may model and adapt some alterations that took place in other animals such as the horse. Finally, in Lesson 17 teams will design their community of organisms and construct models.

Any one or all of these lessons can be expanded. In Lessons 15 and 16, students may wish to research how an environment has already changed. Gathering more details about the evolution of the horse and other animals or plants will help students come up with plausible changes to make in their community of organisms that would help the species adapt to a changed environment. Finally, in Lesson 17, they may wish to build a whole new world, showing a community of organisms in the future.

Teachers' Bookshelf
Gould, Stephen Jay. *Ever Since Darwin: Reflections in Natural History.* New York: Norton, 1979.

Theme Connection: Patterns of Change

Over time, living organisms on the earth have developed many systems for carrying on life processes, including ways of changing and transporting materials. As students work on this project, they can consider the earth's shifting atmosphere and the changes its crust has undergone. Some of these changes may be due to human intervention and invention. In designing their future community of organisms, students will take into account past patterns of change to predict what might happen in the future and how a particular species might adapt to survive in this new world.

Considering Second-Language Learners

As you assign teams for the Think Tank project, group second-language learners with students who are fluent in English. To help second-language learners grasp the task that the team will be working on, draw a time line on the chalkboard. Show the horse's evolution on the time line, but have the line continue past the present time to 1 million years from now. Draw a simple, recognizable organism at the present time and put a question mark 1 million years from now.

As teams work on their projects, encourage them to communicate with words, gestures, and drawings or diagrams.

LESSON 15

THINK TANK

IDENTIFY PROBLEMS:
Designing Future Organisms

Process Skills and Objectives

Students will:

- **predict** the changes in the environment that will bring about changes in a community of organisms in the future

- **compare** photographs of species that have evolved

- **infer** problems an animal or plant will encounter in a changed environment

Opening the Discussion

Begin this Think Tank by having students picture their favorite animal or plant in its natural habitat. Tell them to point out one or two traits that help the plant or animal fit into its environment. Now ask them to imagine that the environment changes. Ask: **What is the new environment like? How would the animal have to change in order to survive in the new environment?** (*Students will probably recall what they've learned about physical adaptations and how traits are passed from parents to their offspring.*) Have students make notes as they think about these questions.

Have students read the Think Tank Road Map on page 58 and read through the problem that they'll be working to solve. Stress that they'll have to make decisions about how the environment is likely to change in the next 1 million years. Ask them to think about how certain diseases may affect their organisms.

**Student Pages
58–59**

Getting Started

⊚ **Troubleshooting:** Students may find it helpful to appoint a group member to write down their ideas as they brainstorm. They can then organize the information after each step.

❶ Remind students that they may choose any animal and/or plant organisms they like. Display pictures of the evolutionary stages of different animals and plants. Have students discuss differences in older and newer forms of related organisms.

LESSON 15

THINK TANK

Identify Problems: **Designing Future Organisms**

Think Tank Road Map

Fossils show that most life forms have been changing slowly over time. There are a lot of reasons for these changes: competition, changing climate, and disease. How will organisms on the earth look one million years from now? Would we recognize them?

15 • In Lesson 15 you'll identify the problems you have to solve in order to design a community of future organisms.

16 • In Lesson 16 you'll find some possible solutions to these problems.

17 • In Lesson 17 you'll make a model based on your design.

You may also want to review the video.

Problem: Your team of scientists has been hired by a movie studio. The studio is making a science fiction film that takes place one million years in the future. Your team's job is to select a community of organisms and redesign them to show how they might change in the next one million years.

⬇ These questions will help you make a list of the problems you'll face while trying to design your organisms of the future.

❶ What have you already learned about the way living things change over time that could help you design your organisms?

❷ Will your organisms be land-dwelling or water-dwelling? What kinds of things will happen to your organisms' environment to affect the way they evolve?

❸ Which characteristics of your organisms will change in one million years? Will your organisms be bigger? smaller? Why will they have to make these changes? What characteristics of your organisms will remain the same?

❹ Will your organisms have greater or fewer enemies? How will they adapt?

❺ Successful organisms are able to change in order to adapt to their environment. As you study the organisms on these pages, ask yourself: In what ways have they changed over time? What caused these changes?

58 THINK TANK

❷ Ask students to consider the climatic changes that could result in land-dwelling or ocean-dwelling organisms 1 million years from now. Ask: **What are some changes that could produce the environmental conditions you predict for 1 million years from now?**

❸ Remind students that certain adaptations in their organism will be passed on if they enable the organism to survive long enough to reproduce.

❹ Students will have to take into account changes that might occur in other animal or plant populations

when they consider changes in the environment.

❺ Help students realize that changes in the organisms' inherited traits were accidental. Changes that ended up helping the organism survive in its environment were passed on to future generations.

After students have read the captions, explain that the rocklike color of the iguana was most likely a variation resulting from a genetic mistake. However, this color probably made it harder for enemies to kill iguanas.

Ask students to make a list of questions they will have to answer in designing their organism.

This is a good time to distribute ThinkMat 15.

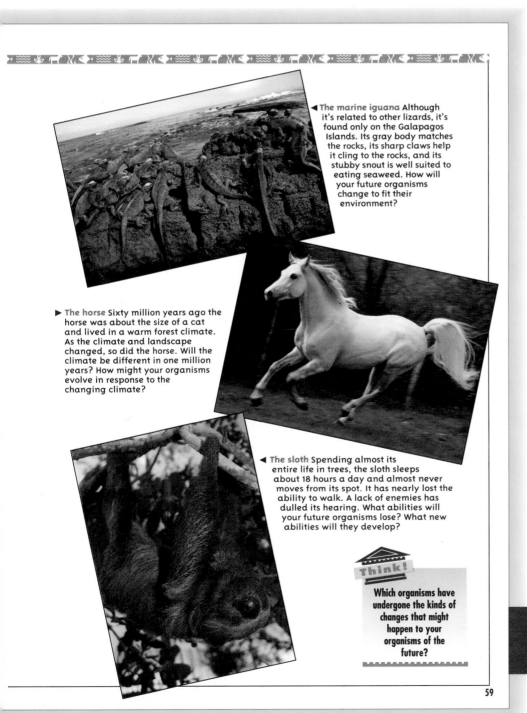

◄ **The marine iguana** Although it's related to other lizards, it's found only on the Galapagos Islands. Its gray body matches the rocks, its sharp claws help it cling to the rocks, and its stubby snout is well suited to eating seaweed. How will your future organisms change to fit their environment?

► **The horse** Sixty million years ago the horse was about the size of a cat and lived in a warm forest climate. As the climate and landscape changed, so did the horse. Will the climate be different in one million years? How might your organisms evolve in response to the changing climate?

◄ **The sloth** Spending almost its entire life in trees, the sloth sleeps about 18 hours a day and almost never moves from its spot. It has nearly lost the ability to walk. A lack of enemies has dulled its hearing. What abilities will your future organisms lose? What new abilities will they develop?

Think!

Which organisms have undergone the kinds of changes that might happen to your organisms of the future?

Think!

By considering the traits of their animal and the environmental changes they have envisioned, students will have some idea of which of the three animals will be most similar to the ones they have chosen.

LESSON THINKING SKILLS:
Organizing Information; Making Generalizations; Identifying Problems

59

FIND SOLUTIONS:
Designing Future Organisms

Process Skills and Objectives

Students will:

- **categorize** problems an organism may face in a changed environment

- **observe** solutions to problems in the case of the evolution of the horse

- **compare** problems and solutions of their chosen organisms with those of the horse

Opening the Discussion

Have students read the text about how scientists do animal restorations. Ask: **Who makes the conclusions about the way extinct animals looked—artists or paleontologists? Why do you think so?** *(Students should realize that paleontologists are more likely to have the knowledge that leads to conclusions about the way extinct animals looked. Their knowledge provides directions for the artists.)* **What might a skeleton be able to tell scientists about an extinct animal— other than such obvious things as its size and number of limbs?** *(Students may mention things like the food it ate, how it walked, and its muscle structure.)*

Read aloud the introductory paragraph on page 60. Ask students how the evolutionary changes in the horse might be like those in their organism. Have someone in each group record their team's responses.

Student Pages 60–61

Keeping It Going

❶ Have teams read through the Exploration steps. As students organize their tables, remind them to leave plenty of space beneath each problem to list a possible solution. Students might want to list each problem or question on a separate sheet of paper in order to have enough room for possible solutions.

❷ As students study the diagram showing the development of the horse, they will probably mention changes in all-over size, form of foot, and length of

---

THINK TANK

Find Solutions: Designing Future Organisms

What's an animal restoration?

How do scientists know what dinosaurs and other extinct animals really looked like? Even if paleontologists are lucky enough to find a complete skeleton, a skeleton is just the framework. What about the other details – facial features, skin color and texture, and scales, for example? Once scientists thought all dinosaurs were drab-looking with grayish, scaly skin. Now they are suggesting that many dinosaurs were actually quite colorful.

Artists work closely with paleontologists to "flesh out" models of animals that no longer exist. They draw conclusions about how the animal may have looked based on what its descendants look like today. They also consider climate and environment. Animals that lived through the ice ages would have needed a thick layer of fat and a heavy coat of fur for warmth. The same guidelines apply when artists and scientists try to imagine what animals might look like in the future.

You just saw some of the ways organisms have slowly changed in response to their environment. Now take a closer look at one organism whose slow but steady evolution has been going on for millions of years – the horse. Studying how the horse has changed may help you solve some problems in designing your organisms of the future.

❶ Make a table of the problems you listed in the last lesson. Beside each problem, try to list a way the horse changed to meet the challenge of a similar problem. You might not always be able to think of a matching problem.

❷ Study the diagrams. Which features of the horse have changed the most as *Hyracotherium* became *Equus*? Which features haven't changed at all? How will this help you design your organisms of the future?

❸ Below each problem you listed in designing your organisms of the future, record any solutions you can think of. List the characteristics of each organism that will change. Next to each characteristic, tell how and why it will change. Use both words and pictures.

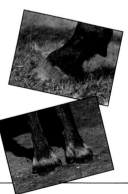

How does the foot of the modern horse compare with that of *Mesohippus*?

leg. Features that haven't changed include shape of head, short hair, and mode of locomotion. Help students to see that they don't have to change everything about their animal, but that what they do change should be in response to a change in the environment.

❸ Student teams might want to do more research on the evolutionary history of organisms other than the horse. This will help students see how certain environmental changes resulted in the adaptation of other species, and enable them to think of possible

solutions for designing an organism in the future. Remind teams to make drawings to show ways certain characteristics might change. Have them use captions and labels with the drawings.

This is a good time to distribute ThinkMat 16.

DEVELOPMENT OF THE MODERN HORSE

Hyracotherium
Sixty million years ago, *Hyracotherium* lived in the forest and ate leaves. Its four-toed front feet and its doglike pads may have helped it to move on the soft ground and step carefully in the forest.

Mesohippus
Forty million years ago the climate began to get cooler. Grasslands had started to grow, and *Mesohippus*'s teeth had changed as its food supply changed. Its middle toe got longer, making it easier to move on the harder ground. *Mesohippus* got bigger and faster, which may have helped it to escape its predators.

Merychippus
Twenty-five million years ago the grasslands had spread as the climate became even drier. *Merychippus* now had only one toe for galloping on the hard ground. Its eyes were higher on its head, which may have helped it to see its predators even while grazing.

Equus
Two million years ago the climate had changed even more, and *Equus*—the modern horse—evolved. *Equus* is the biggest and fastest of the horses. It changed as its predators got bigger and faster, too.

Other resources you can check:
• To find out about the fossil record of dinosaurs: *Eyewitness Books: Dinosaur*, by David Norman, Ph.D., and Angela Milner, Ph.D. Alfred A. Knopf, 1989.

• To find out how humans have developed: *Traces of Life: The Origins of Humankind*, by Kathryn Lasky. Morrow Junior Books, 1989.

Think!

How can looking at the way the horse developed help you design your future organisms?

Think!

After working on this lesson, students will probably be able to think of many examples of how looking at solutions to one problem can help in solving another. If they're having difficulty with this question, suggest they look over their tables.

LESSON THINKING SKILLS:
Making Analogies; Identifying and Suggesting Alternatives; Solving Problems

MAKE MODELS:
Designing Future Organisms

Process Skills and Objectives

Students will:

- **make models** of a community of organisms in the future

- **communicate** their ideas about their redesigned plants and animals

Opening the Discussion

Read through the possible models that students can use for their animals. Invite students to suggest other ideas. They might even like to make a model that combines two or more of the ideas listed. Ask: **What advantage would a written description or oral presentation have over physical models?** *(Answers will vary, but students will probably realize that with written and oral models they wouldn't be limited by the type of materials available—as they would with physical models.)*

Emphasize that each team member must participate in making decisions about the model, such as what the changes in the future organisms will be.

Putting It All Together

❶ Students might want to refer to their LabMats before deciding exactly how their organisms will change. Changes should enable the organisms to survive in the altered environment that the students have envisioned.

❷ Explain that planning needs to come before building. You might have students plan one day and begin building the next day so they have a chance to gather materials from home.

Make Models: Designing Future Organisms

Possible models for your organisms:

Diagram Use the diagrams in Lessons 1–14 to help you draw a large diagram showing your community of organisms. Be sure to include labels explaining why your organisms changed.

3-Dimensional Model Use clay, sticks, or any combination of materials to build a model of your community of future organisms.

Written Description Write a report that carefully describes the characteristics of the organisms in your community. Tell why your organisms changed the way they did.

Computer Graphics Use a graphics program to design your future organisms on the computer.

Oral Presentation Give an oral presentation explaining your community of organisms to the producers and directors of the movie. You can use visual aids such as tables and drawings.

Your team has identified problems you'll face in trying to design a community of organisms that might have developed on the earth in one million years. You've also identified possible solutions to some of these problems. Now it's time to put those solutions to work.

❶ Work with your team to design a community of future organisms. List all the features that will have changed on these organisms over the next million years. Explain why they will have changed.

❷ Make a model based on your design. You and your team will probably decide that some of the models shown to the left will work better than others for showing your organisms. Gather the materials you need and start working.

❸ Look at the models your class has made. How did different teams solve different problems? Did everybody think their organisms would face the same problems? Did they come up with the same solutions?

❹ How would your model have been different if you hadn't learned how traits are passed from one generation to the next? How did knowing about natural selection help you design your community of organisms? What were the most important things you learned in this unit that helped you design your organisms of the future?

❸ Allow time for students to look at one another's work, jotting down reactions and questions about each model.

❹ Have students imagine what kind of model they would have built before studying about how traits are passed down and how natural selection works. Then allow time for a general discussion about any new ideas that went into their Think Tank project.

This is a good time to distribute ThinkMat 17.

Wrapping It Up

Here's a new problem: Suppose that the type of tree that houses and feeds the three-toed sloth is dying out because it is being attacked by a mutation of a formerly harmless insect. Encourage students to think about how artificial selection could be used to help the sloth survive. Ask: **What things related to breeding could humans do to ensure the survival of the sloth in its present form?** *(Answers will vary. Humans could breed trees with characteristics that would make the trees less attractive to the insects, or they could try to breed sloths that could eat the leaves of another kind of tree.)*

This would be a good opportunity for students to get on-line to share ideas about their future organisms.

Think!

By actually creating models, students will be able to see how certain characteristics in their organisms may be more problematic than they initially perceived. Students will be able to determine such things as whether the length of an organism's legs need to be changed to support its body weight, or whether it needs a larger skull, and so forth.

Resources for designing your team's organisms:

• Take a look at your journals and LabMats from this unit. They have data you've collected and conclusions you've made about how organisms change over time.

• The graphics and information in Lessons 1–14 of this *Student's Map to Exploration* will also help you to design your organisms.

• The reference books you've used in this unit are filled with information about how organisms change and adapt.

• Check the Video Clue Log to see how the Science Sleuths investigated the ways living things change.

• Are you faced with a really hard problem? Trade information with another team to see how others may have solved this problem.

Think!

How did making models of your future organisms help you think of problems and solutions you missed before?

LESSON THINKING SKILLS:
Visualizing; Making Decisions; Judging and Evaluating

63

Unit Assessment

Assessment Objectives

- Assess students' understanding of the unit concepts as reflected in their writing and their approaches to solving problems.

- Acknowledge different developmental levels and learning styles.

- Monitor each student's developmental growth.

- Assess progress in mastery of process skills.

- Assess progress in mastery of thinking skills.

Addressing Different Learning Styles

Students learn in a variety of ways. A wide variety of assessment options are offered to help you meet the needs of visual, auditory, and kinesthetic learners.

Often students gain new understanding as they approach concepts through different modalities. Students and teachers can benefit from using different types of options, including hands-on, writing and speaking, and pencil and paper activities.

Assessing Second-Language Learners

Make sure you don't overlook second-language learners' understanding of concepts. If they're having difficulty with a task, ask yourself if the difficulty is due to a lack of English proficiency or a genuine lack of understanding of the concept. Assess their understanding by asking for nonverbal responses, such as pointing, or by asking questions that require one-word responses.

Using Benchmarks

Student Benchmarks provide criteria that you can use to judge how well your students understand each lesson. Think of the benchmarks not as rigid requirements but as indicators of progress.

Benchmarks are not a list of facts that students should recall but descriptions of how students respond when they understand ideas. You'll note three levels of understanding described. The novice has achieved some familiarity with concepts but may not be able to explain ideas in new ways or to visualize how information fits into a bigger picture. The apprentice can discuss concepts and communicate ideas in his or her own words but may still be having difficulty applying knowledge to new situations. The proficient student has reached a level of understanding that involves application, synthesis, and exploration.

Quite intentionally, Student Benchmarks show a progression. While the benchmarks describe objective skills and concepts, they also reflect that learning is a process of growth and that the goal of teaching is to lead all students to the proficient level.

You know your students best. Your knowledge, in combination with Student Benchmarks, will help you evaluate progress as you lead your students toward a deeper understanding of the material.

Using the Assessment Chart

The Assessment Chart provided with this lesson makes it easy for you to record the acquisition of process skills and conceptual understanding. You can use this chart in several ways: You can make a copy of the chart for each unit and put students' names in the first column; you can make copies of the chart for each lesson, listing students' names in the first column; or you can make copies of the chart for each student, listing the lesson titles in the first column. This table, along with anecdotal records, will help you follow each student's progress.

Assessment Chart

Record Lesson Assessment **Record Unit Assessment** **Refer to chart for lesson planning.**

KEY
- • Proficient
- + Apprentice
- - Novice

UNIT:

Process Check:

(Student's name or lesson name)	Observing	Communicating	Comparing	Ordering	Categorizing	Predicting	Inferring	Measuring	Experimenting	Hypothesizing	Controlling Variables	Interpreting Data	Making Models	Operational Definitions	Recognizing Relationships												

Performance Assessment

Process Skills and Concepts

Preparing for the Assessment

Materials per Group: LabMat 18, paper, pencil, clay, pictures and books about fossils and prehistoric life forms

Suggested Grouping: individual or groups of four

Approximate Time: 40 minutes

Student Benchmarks: Process Skills

Proficient: Students' lists are comprehensive and reflect what they know about animal and plant fossils described in the unit. Their models show they're using their knowledge along with process skills such as observing, comparing, inferring, and making models.

Apprentice: Students list several things they can tell from fossil bones. Their models and responses will show they're using process skills such as comparing and inferring.

Novice: Students will list one or two things they can tell from bones, but their models may not describe much about their animals.

Classroom Management: Make a copy of LabMat 18 for each student. To assess the process development of individual students, have them do the Performance Assessment on their own.

EXPLORATION: Make some bones.

1. Ask students what kinds of things fossil bones can tell about an animal. Distribute LabMat 18 and have students list some things bones can tell us. They may want to add some examples that they know about.

2. Have the materials available to students. Tell them that their assignment is to make up an animal that might once have lived on the earth, choose an environment and way of life for it, and then make models of a few bones that would tell others important things about it. Allow them to use books about fossils to guide them. After students have made their bones, have them exhibit them to the rest of the class, who will try to infer as much as they can about the animal. Students may want to compare pictures of fossils with the model bones.

Troubleshooting: Encourage students to list some traits of their animal and how it lives. They might want to sketch it before deciding which bones to model.

3. Students should not model an entire skeleton, but only a few (three or four) representative bones (teeth count!). Encourage them to make their bones proportional and to scale. That is, if the animal's front legs are tiny and the back ones much larger, the models should reflect this difference. If students imagine a huge animal, they should make the bones small and tell the class the scale they used. What bones would be most important in telling what kind of food their animal ate? What might the legs of a fast-moving animal look like?

4. The point of the activity is for students to make inferences about the animal's appearance and way of life, not to guess its identity or figure out everything about it. Encourage students to give the reasons for making their models as they did and for the inferences they make about other models.

Connected Thinking

Thinking Skills and Concepts

The Idea

By writing two narratives describing situations in which the community of organisms they designed for the Think Tank would become extinct or survive by adapting, students will have an opportunity to demonstrate their understanding of the ways living things evolve.

Assignment

Think about the community of organisms your team designed for the Think Tank. What kind of environment did you choose for it? Think of some things that could happen to it or its environment that might be a problem. Using what you know about extinction, variation, adaptation, and natural selection, write an essay about two possible fates for one of your organisms. Tell how and why your organism ends up as it does.

Planning

Allow students time to meet with their teams to discuss the community of organisms they designed. What adaptations did the animal have that helped it survive in its environment?

Writing

As students write their essays, they may want to consider the following questions:

- Is my point of view clearly stated?

- Have I given logical reasons that explain why my organisms may change in this way?

- Do the sentences in each of my paragraphs flow logically from one to another?

Presenting

As an alternative to writing, or as a follow-up activity, students might want to present their descriptions as comic strips. Each panel of the strip should depict a stage in the extinction or adaptation of their organism. If necessary, they may label each panel with a brief descriptive caption.

Student Benchmarks: Thinking Skills

Proficient: Students' essays describe in detail the causes and effects in the way living things change. Their conclusions are based on their Think Tank investigation and Explorations from the unit.

Apprentice: Students show some recognition of causes and effects, but they may miss some stages in the processes. Examples come from their Think Tank or Explorations from the unit.

Novice: Students describe what happens to their animal in each situation they think of, but they may not show clear and plausible causes and effects leading to their results.

Follow-Up on Baseline Assessment

The Baseline Assessment allows you to identify where each student conceptually starts the unit. By repeating the same assessment task, you can better understand and share with students the growth they have demonstrated throughout the unit.

In Lesson 1, students pretended to be taking a ride in a machine that carried them back through time. They wrote three journal entries describing the kinds of living things they saw on the earth 10,000 years ago, 140 million years ago, and at the time just after the earth began. You saved these journal entries. Have students write three more journal entries now. Then pass out their original entries and have them compare the two.

Use these journal entries and the students' comparisons of them as an informal assessment of what each student has learned about the unit. Note whether or not they have increased their understanding of the ways living things change over time.

Portfolio Assessment:

Student Portfolio

As you begin the unit, provide each student with a folder or folded piece of 11" × 17" construction paper to use as a Portfolio. In each unit you will find suggestions for Portfolio ideas. At the end of the unit, encourage each student to put together items from their collected files. The goal is for each student to select work according to personally defined criteria. You might suggest the following:

1 This Surprised Me the Most (new idea)

2 I Really Liked the Way It Looks (art/design)

3 I Thought This Would Be Hard (meets a challenge)

4 We Did a Great Job Together (cooperative effort)

5 This Helps Me Remember What I Learned (good explanation/description)

6 This Explains Something I've Been Wondering About (insight/understanding)

Teacher Portfolio

Prepare a folder of your written remarks and add to it at convenient intervals. Use classroom anecdotes and notes about students' performances based generally upon the following criteria:

1 Follows instructions

2 Actively participates

3 Explores further

4 Applies information to new situations

Troubleshooting: Write or type each student's name on a label and photocopy it onto multiple sheets of labels. Attach the labels to a clipboard. Notes about each student can be written on his or her label and later peeled off and stuck in your portfolio.

Assessing Cooperative Groups

When students work together on a project, it's often hard to determine which part of the project was done by which student. A group evaluation is always easier. To determine individual strengths, observe the role each student assumes in a group. You can also assign specific roles to students. Here are some roles to watch for or assign:

Coordinator: one who brings the group together and assigns tasks

Coach: one who encourages other members

Reminder: one who reminds the group of the details of an activity

Helper: one who helps others in the group

Inventor: one who has creative ideas

Reporter: one who records and expresses the group's ideas

Problem-solver: one who suggests ways to overcome obstacles

Written Tests

Three ThinkMats are provided for reviewing the unit. They appear at the end of each subconcept in Lessons 5, 10, and 14. They can be used as an ongoing review or at the end of the unit as a unit review. In addition, ThinkMat 18 is a three-page scorable test for the unit.

Self-Assessment for the Teacher

How Is It Working?

Stop at convenient intervals while you're using this program and ask yourself the following questions:

- Am I helping my students to make connections between ideas?

- Am I adjusting my teaching methods to address the needs and strengths of my class?

- Do I model a positive attitude about the value of science learning?

- Does my classroom promote cooperative learning and discovery?

Self-Assessment Questions

Photocopy this page and use the evaluation code (-; +; •) from the Assessment Chart to monitor your teaching success periodically.

❶ Make connections? _ _ _ _ _ _ _

❷ Adjust methods? _ _ _ _ _ _ _

❸ Model attitude? _ _ _ _ _ _ _

❹ Promote discovery? _ _ _ _ _ _ _

FOR SCIENCE BROWSERS

Sharks
by Susan McGrath
Excerpt from *National Geographic World*

Not mindless monsters, sharks are more intelligent than once thought. They possess highly developed senses, also. And a chemical compound that seems to help sharks fight off infections may someday help doctors treat humans.

As for their killer reputation, very few shark species attack humans, and then only under certain conditions. People kill more than 100 *million* sharks a year. So many sharks have been killed that scientists fear some species may be wiped out.

The oceans would be a very different place without sharks. As predators at the top of the oceans' food chain, large sharks play an important role in keeping the populations of other species in check. Part of their job is to weed out weak and injured animals, leaving the healthiest to reproduce.

Concerned scientists are working with government officials to put reasonable limits on shark fishing. If they succeed, sharks will survive and maintain a useful place in the oceans of the world.—*February, 1994*

Scientists Dig Up New Dinosaurs

by Sean McCollum
from *Scholastic News*

Scientists recently found the bones of a dinosaur fiercer than *Tyrannosaurus rex*. Other fossil-finders dug up the skeleton of one of the first dinosaurs ever to roam the Earth.

Why are dinosaurs making such big news 65 million years after they became extinct? Dr. James Kirkland is a scientist who studies fossils. "There's new dinosaur research going on all over the world," he told *SN*. In the past, some governments blocked dinosaur research in their countries. In other places, wars kept research from getting done. That is changing now.

Digging for Dinos

In 1991, Dr. Kirkland was part of a team hunting for dinosaur fossils in Utah. While they were digging up one skeleton, a worker found a giant claw. "It was the largest I had ever seen," Dr. Kirkland told *SN*. The claw belonged to a new kind of dinosaur. They named it . *Utahraptor (Yew-tah-rap-ter)*.

Scientists can tell a lot about how a dinosaur lived by studying its bones. They think Utahraptor was about 20 feet long and weighed 1,500 pounds. The way its legs were built tells scientists that Utahraptor was a good runner. And its 15-inch claws show that it was a killer. "This killer claw was an incredibly powerful cutting tool," Dr. Kirkland says. That's why Utahraptor got the nickname "superslasher." Dr. Kirkland thinks Utahraptor would have used its claws to kick and slash other dinosaurs.

Utahraptor isn't the only exciting fossil found recently. In 1991 in South America, Dr. Paul Sereno dug up the skeleton of one of the first dinosaurs. He named it *Eoraptor (EE-oh-rap-ter)*. "Eoraptor gives us a picture of what the earliest dinosaurs were like," Dr. Sereno says. It was only about the size of a goose. Scientists think it lived about 225 million years ago.

Each new fossil gives scientists new clues about dinosaurs and how they lived. "New information is popping up all the time," says Dr. Kirkland. He expects many more exciting dinosaur discoveries in the years to come. —*March, 1993* ◆

Now That's An Old Tree!

A kind of tree found commonly in cities is one of the oldest trees on the planet. The gingko, with leaves that look like pale green fans, had relatives that were alive during the age of dinosaurs.

Keeping An Eye On the Bird

Scientists have identified about 9,000 species of birds. Because their habitats are being destroyed, especially in rain forests and wetlands, 6,000 species are losing members rapidly, and 1,000 species are in danger of becoming extinct.

Dinosaurs—My Life's Work

by Sam Curtis
from *Boy's Life*

When Jack Horner is on the job, he lives in a tepee. And he hunts from sunup to sundown across the eroded plains of Montana.

"When I'm walking around in the field looking for things, I run across rattlesnakes and, occasionally, grizzly bears," Horner says. He is curator of paleontology at the Museum of the Rockies in Bozeman, Mont. Or, put another way, he is a dinosaur hunter.

Horner finds dinosaurs in the form of fossilized bones. He uses those bones to help scientists understand how dinosaurs lived when they ruled the earth more than 65 million years ago.

Dinosaur bones are usually buried in rock. To locate a good spot to hunt for them, Horner uses a geologic map.

"I just look up the geologic age in which dinosaurs lived," Horner says. "I look on the map to see where that rock is exposed at the surface of the ground. And then I walk around in those areas looking for bones."

During the winter, when bad weather keeps him indoors, Horner studies the bones for clues to figure out how the dinosaurs lived.

"It's like being a detective," Horner says. "A detective has a crime scene. From that scene, he has to reconstruct what happened.

I reconstruct the evidence the same way a detective does."

Horner is so good at finding and interpreting dinosaur bones that he is considered one of the foremost paleontologists in the world. In 1978, he discovered the first nest of baby dinosaurs ever found. The nest was the first evidence that dinosaurs cared for their young. These were a type of hadrosaur, which Horner named *Maiasaura,* or Good Mother Lizard. He named the nesting site Egg Mountain.

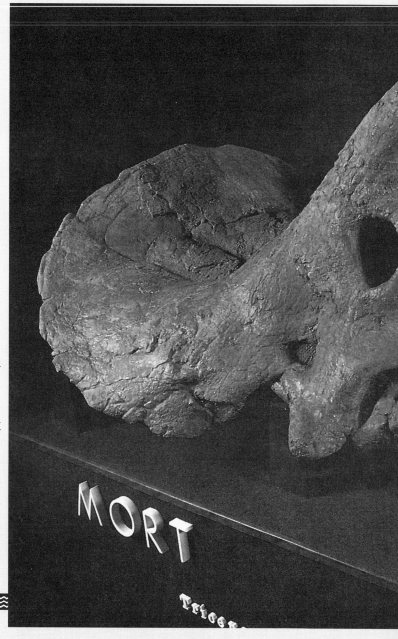

"The discoveries of Egg Mountain and that area put us into a new realm of understanding dinosaur behavior," he says. "We got down to knowing how dinosaurs laid their eggs, how they took care of their young, how they herded and migrated. We learned all sorts of things that people hadn't even guessed at before."

Horner's interest in dinosaurs goes back to his first fossil find at age 7. Later, after attending the University of Montana, he became a preparator at Princeton University.

A preparator digs bones out of the ground. Then, in the museum's laboratory, he or she cleans off the bones and tries to fit them together so a paleontologist can study them.

In 1982, by then a paleontologist himself, Horner became curator of vertebrate paleontology at the Museum of the Rockies. He is also a professor of paleontology at Montana State University.

"I try to encourage my students to be the best."

Horner says some people romanticize his job and assume that he is a daring adventurer like Indiana Jones. Actually, the job is mostly hard work. But he also admits that he wouldn't be a dinosaur hunter if it were not exciting.

"It really *is* exciting to find something that no one has ever seen before and that gives you information no one has ever had.

"But getting the stuff out of the ground when it's snowing and blowing 40 miles an hour can be miserable. Of course, it can get to be 110 degrees with no shade too.

"I don't think it's possible to encourage anyone to do this kind of work," Horner continues. "If you really want to do it, you will. If you're only slightly interested in it, you will never make it." — *February, 1992* ◄

Jack Horner likes dinosaurs so much he makes his living digging them out of the ground.

Another Wonder of the Rain Forest

Brazil's rapidly disappearing rain forest is the home of a newly discovered species of monkey, the Rio Maues marmoset. The discovery of an unknown insect species doesn't surprise scientists, but finding an unknown mammal like a new marmoset is— and this is the third unknown species of monkey discovered in the Amazon rain forest during the last three years.

Excerpt from *The Life and Letters of Charles Darwin*

Edited by his son, Francis Darwin

C. Darwin to Asa Gray.
September 10, [1866?]

. . . . I have just begun a large course of experiments on the germination of the seed, and on the growth of the young plants when raised from a pistil fertilised by pollen from the same flower, and from pollen from a distinct plant of the same, or of some other variety. I have not made sufficient experiments to judge certainly, but in some cases the difference in the growth of the young plants is highly remarkable. I have taken every kind of precaution in getting seed from the same plant, in germinating the seed on my own chimneypiece, in planting the seedlings in the same flower-pot, and under this similar treatment I have seen the young seedlings from the crossed seed exactly twice as tall

Fossil Whale Feet: A Step in Evolution

by R. Monastersky
from *Science News*

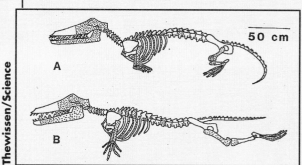

Thewissen/Science

Paleontologists digging in Pakistan have discovered the 50-million-year-old remains of a whale with legs and feet.

The new-found fossil, called *Ambulocetus natans*, is the first known ancient whale with large hind limbs, says J.G.M. Thewissen of the Northeastern Ohio Universities College of Medicine in Rootstown. He and his colleagues report their find in the Jan. 14 Science.

Paleontologist Annalisa Berta of San Diego State University calls *Ambulocetus* "a very significant discovery. It shows us for the first time a whale that had well-developed hind limbs. It's very clear this animal was using its hind limbs in locomotion."

Researchers believe that modern whales descended from four-legged carnivorous mammals, somewhat like large wolves, that once roamed the continents. Sometime around the start of the Eocene period, 57 million years ago, these carnivores gave up their dry lifestyle for one under the waves. Ancient whales lost their legs and pelvises and developed the fluked tail that propels these modern leviathans through the seas.

Living whales have no visible hind limbs, but some have internal finger-size bones that are vestiges of hips and legs, an indication that they evolved from land creatures.
—January, 1994 ◆

(above, left) Ambulocetus standing on land (A) and swimming (B).

as the seedlings from the self-fertilised seed; both seeds having germinated on the same day. If I can establish this fact (but perhaps it will all go to the dogs), in some fifty cases, with plants of different orders, I think it will be very important, for then we shall positively know why the structure of every flower permits, or favours, or necessitates an occasional cross with a distinct individual. But all this is rather cooking my hare before I have caught it. But somehow it is a great pleasure to me to tell you what I am about. Believe me, my dear Gray,

Ever yours most truly, and with cordial thanks,

Ch. Darwin.

—© Copyright, 1889 ◆

Culver Pictures, Inc.

We Invited Carp to America

by Dick Pryce
Excerpt from *Boy's Life*

Next time you catch a carp while fishing for something else, don't get too angry. Although some anglers might not like this fish today, nobody complained in 1876 when the United States Fish Commission imported it from Germany.

Carp were, and still are, great favorites in Europe and Asia. There was no reason to suspect the fish would not be welcome in North America.

German carp, whose ancestors came from Asia, were released in Maryland ponds in the late 1800's. They multiplied. In a few years, the fish commission had too many so it offered the carp to members of Congress in Washington, D.C.

The congressmen gave carp to supporters back home. In this way, carp were "planted" all over the United States.

Very quickly the carp spread. They began to compete with native fish such as walleye, catfish, trout and bass. As their numbers grew, carp took over in rivers and lakes.

Carp are omnivorous, that is, they eat vegetable matter as well as meat. By rooting for plant food in the shallows, carp kick up sediment, creating a muddy environment in which most native fish can't live. Carp survive in muddy, dirty, warm water.

Because the carp competes with more popular fish, most Americans reject it. Many anglers also don't think carp are very tasty. —*January, 1991* ◆

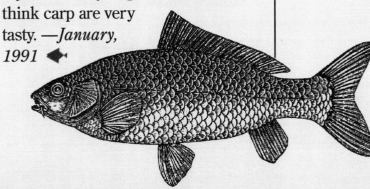

Resources

More Literature for Students

Baylor, Byrd. *If You Are a Hunter of Fossils.* New York: Macmillan, 1984.

Cole, Joanna. *Evolution: The Story of How Life Developed on Earth.* New York: Harper, 1989.

Cole, Sheila. *The Dragon in the Cliff.* New York: Lothrop, Lee, and Shepard, 1991.

Cork, Barbara and Lynn Bresler. *The Usborne Young Scientist: Evolution.* Tulsa, OK: EDC Publishing, 1985.

Lasky, Kathryn. *Traces of Life.* New York: Morrow, 1989.

Liptak, Karen. *Pangaea, the Mother Continent.* Tuscon, AZ: Harbinger House, 1989.

McCord, Anne. *Prehistoric Life.* Tulsa, OK: EDC Publishing, 1993.

Norman, David, and Engela Milner. *Eyewitness Books: Dinosaur.* New York: Knopf, 1989.

Skelton, Renee. *Charles Darwin and the Theory of Natural Selection.* Hauppauge, NY: Barron's Educational Series, 1987.

Taylor, Paul D. *Eyewitness Books: Fossil.* New York: Alfred A. Knopf, 1990.

Literature for Teachers

Attenborough, David. *The Living Planet: A Portrait of the Earth.* Boston: Little, Brown, 1986.

Bakker, Robert T. *The Dinosaur Heresies: New Theories Unlocking the Mystery of the Dinosaurs and Their Extinction.* New York: Zebra, 1988.

Daugherty, Belinda. "The Great Bone Search," *Science and Children.* October 1993, pp.14–16.

Eldredge, Niles. *Lifepulse: Episodes from the Story of the Fossil Record.* New York: Facts on File, 1987.

Gould, Stephen Jay. *Ever Since Darwin: Reflections in Natural History.* New York: Norton, 1979.

Gould, Stephen Jay. *Hen's Teeth and Horse's Toes.* New York: Norton, 1984.

Gould, Stephen Jay. *The Flamingo's Smile: Reflections in Natural History.* New York: Norton, 1987.

Hickman, Pamela. *Birdwise.* Reading, MA: Addison-Wesley, 1989.

Horner, John K. and James Gorman. *Digging Dinosaurs.* New York: Harper, 1990.

Jastrow, Robert. *The Enchanted Loom.* New York: Simon and Schuster, 1981.

Johanson, Donald E. *Lucy: The Beginning of Humankind.* New York: Simon and Schuster, 1990.

Equipment

Nonconsumables Provided with Unit	Lesson
magnifying glass, 8	2
fossil kit, 4	2, 5
spoons, 1 package of 24	3, 11
numbered cube, 16	7, 10
kidney seeds, 1 lb	11
spotted seeds, 1 lb	11
white seeds, 1 lb	11
wax bean seeds, 1 lb	7, 10

Available in the Consumable Kit	Lesson
punch-out fossil kit, 8	2
clay powder, 1 lb	3
paper cups, 8	3
dried bees, 8	3
mucilage, 6 containers	3
petroleum jelly, 1 jar	3
plaster of paris, 2 1/2 lb box	3
sand, 1 kg	3
adding machine tape, 1 roll of 165 ft	5
peanuts, in shell, 3 bags	8
plastic cups, 50	11
modeling clay, 2 lbs, (4 colors)	13
toothpicks	13

Classroom Supplies	Lesson
ruler	2, 5, 8
water	3
leaves and other thin objects	3
scissors	4, 7, 9, 11
adhesive tape	5, 9, 13
markers or crayons	5, 9
paper	7, 9
coins	7, 9
pencil or pen	7, 8, 10, 11, 13
forks	11
watch or clock with second hand	11
black paper	11

Recyclables for Students to Bring*	Lesson
margarine tub	3
clothespin	11

*Referenced in the **Home Connection** letter